2⁰⁰

THE
CARUS MATHEMATICAL MONOGRAPHS

Published by

THE MATHEMATICAL ASSOCIATION OF AMERICA

———

Publication Committee

THE CARUS MATHEMATICAL MONO-
GRAPHS are an expression of the desire of
Mrs. Mary Hegeler Carus, and of her son,
Dr. Edward H. Carus, to contribute to the dis-
semination of mathematical knowledge by making
accessible at nominal cost a series of expository
presentations of the best thoughts and keenest
researches in pure and applied mathematics. The
publication of these monographs was made possible by a notable gift to the Mathematical Association of America by Mrs. Carus as sole trustee
of the Edward C. Hegeler Trust Fund. The
expositions of mathematical subjects which the
monographs will contain are to be set forth in a
manner comprehensible not only to teachers and
students specializing in mathematics, but also to
scientific workers in other fields, and especially
to the wide circle of thoughtful people who, having
a moderate acquaintance with elementary mathematics, wish to extend their knowledge without
prolonged and critical study of the mathematical
journals and treatises. The scope of this series
includes also historical and biographical monographs.

The following books in this series have been
published to date:
No. 1. *Calculus of Variations*, by PROFESSOR
G. A. BLISS. (First Impression in 1925, Second
Impression in 1927.)
No. 2. *Analytic Functions of a Complex Variable*,
by PROFESSOR D. R. CURTISS. (First Impres-
sion, 1926.)
No. 3. *Mathematical Statistics*, by PROFESSOR
H. L. RIETZ. (First Impression, April, 1927,
Second Impression, September, 1929.)
No. 4. *Projective Geometry*, by PROFESSOR J. W.
YOUNG. (First Impression, March, 1930.)

The Carus Mathematical Monographs

NUMBER FOUR

PROJECTIVE GEOMETRY

By
JOHN WESLEY YOUNG
Professor of Mathematics, Dartmouth College

Published for
THE MATHEMATICAL ASSOCIATION OF AMERICA
by
THE OPEN COURT PUBLISHING COMPANY
CHICAGO, ILLINOIS

Composed, Printed and Bound by
The Collegiate Press
George Banta Publishing Company
Menasha, Wisconsin, U. S. A.

PREFACE

Projective Geometry may be approached by various routes: postulational or intuitive, synthetic or analytic, metric or purely projective. In a monograph which is to give a first approach to the subject it has seemed to me that the treatment should be based on intuition, should develop the subject by synthetic methods, and should keep projective properties sharply distinguished from the metric specializations. The reader will accordingly find in the first five chapters a systematic and thoroughly elementary treatment of the most fundamental propositions of projective geometry, culminating in the theorems of Pascal and Brianchon and the polar system of a conic. My purpose in these chapters has been to develop on an intuitive basis the concepts and the properties of projective space, without any admixture of metric ideas. Only in this way, I believe, can the reader gain a clear impression of what the word projective implies.

A monograph on projective geometry, however, which aims at some degree of comprehensiveness can not stop there. Much of the beauty and value of the subject lies in its relation to metric geometries, and the foundation for the use of analytic methods should at least be laid. Accordingly, I devote the remaining chapters to such additional aspects of our subject in order to fill in and round out the picture. Chapter VI, devoted to a first introduction to the metric specialization of projective theorems, is still thoroughly elementary. Beginning with Chapter VII, however, the treatment will make somewhat greater demands on the reader's mathematical maturity, since it is based on the group concept. After a preliminary Chapter (VII), Chapter VIII lays the foundation for the use of analytic methods and Chapter IX discusses metric properties from the more general standpoint of the group to which a geometry belongs.

In writing this monograph I have, of course, made free use of the text by Professor Veblen and myself, *Projective Geometry*, two volumes, Ginn & Company (the second volume by Professor Veblen alone). I have also found Professor Severi's *Geometria Proiettiva* very useful in certain parts of my work. I am greatly indebted to the other members of the editorial committee of the Carus Monographs, Professors Slaught, Bliss, Curtis and Kempner, for many valuable criticisms and suggestions resulting from their careful reading of the manuscript and the proof sheets. Especially must I express my gratitude and appreciation to Professor Slaught for the large amount of painstaking and time-consuming work which he put on the task of seeing the little book through the press, especially in its earlier stages when I was abroad. If this monograph proves to be a worthy companion for the earlier members of the monograph family, it will be very largely due to the unselfish efforts of these friends.

J. W. YOUNG

HANOVER, NEW HAMPSHIRE
   November, 1929

TABLE OF CONTENTS

CHAPTER I

INTRODUCTORY CONCEPTIONS

1. Perspective drawing. Projective geometry like many another mathematical discipline has its historical origin in a practical problem: How to draw a picture in a plane that shall represent a three-dimensional object in such a way that the various portions of the picture, in their mutual relations, present the same aspect as do the corresponding visible portions of the object. Among the first to consider this problem of perspective drawing in a scientific way was Leonardo da Vinci (1452–1519), whose fame is perhaps greatest as a painter, but who according to more recent research must also be classed as a great pioneer in the domain of science.

The geometric formulation of the problem, as conceived by Leonardo, is as follows: From every visible point of a given three-dimensional object rays of light enter the eye of the observer. If a transparent plate be inserted between the eye and the object, each of these rays pierces the plate in a definite point, which is the image of the corresponding point of the object. The aggregate of all these points on the plate constitutes the desired picture. The problem consists of finding out how to draw the picture without the intervention of the transparent plate. We may note in passing that the photographic camera accomplishes precisely this feat when it collects the rays from the object in its lens, the "eye of the camera," and projects them on the sensitized plate. That the plate is in this case behind the "eye," rather than in front of it, is obviously an unimportant difference.

2. Projection and section. Correspondence. By considering in more detail the nature of the process just described, we shall become familiar with one of the fundamental processes of projective geometry, and shall also get a glimpse of some of the characteristics of this geometry which differentiate it from the more familiar, so-called metric, geometry of our school days.

The purely geometric description of the process suggested by Leonardo consists of two parts: From a point O lines are drawn to every point of a geometric figure F; these lines issuing from O are cut by a plane ω. We may now make our first definition.

The set of lines joining a point O to the points of a figure F is called the *projection of F from O*. If a set of lines issuing from a point O is cut by a plane ω, the set of points in which the plane ω cuts the lines through O is called the *section* of the lines through O by the plane ω.

This process of projection and section is fundamental in projective geometry. By means of it, to every point of the figure F is made to correspond a definite line through O, and in general, to every line through O is made to correspond a definite point on ω. Certain exceptions to this statement which may arise will be considered presently. The concept thus suggested of a correspondence between the elements of two figures is of fundamental importance. We shall, therefore, give a formal definition of it.

The elements of two geometric figures are said to be in *reciprocally one-to-one correspondence*, by some definite process (as for example, by the process of projection and section just described), if to every element of one figure is made to correspond a uniquely determined element of the other, and, vice-versa, if every element of the second figure is the correspondent of a uniquely determined element of the first.

If now we return to our problem of perspective drawing, we see that the picture on the transparent plate

FIG. 1.

between the object and the eye of the artist is the figure obtained by means of a projection from the eye of the observer and a section (of this projection) by the plane of the transparent plate. If the reader will consider the nature of any perspective representation, for example the adjoined photograph of a court in the Palazzo Vecchio in Florence, he will recognize the following characteristics: A straight line in the original object is represented in the photograph by a straight line. This must be the case, since all the lines through the center of projection and the points of a given line lie in a plane and the section of this plane by the plane of section must be a straight line. The intersection of two straight lines, that is a point, of the original is represented by the intersection of the corresponding lines in the photograph. An angle of the original will be represented by an angle in the photograph, but *not* in general *by an angle of the same size*. A right angle in the original, for example, may be represented by either an acute or an obtuse angle in the picture. The reader will observe a number of examples in the adjoined photograph. He should, however, not content himself by merely observing the fact, but should make clear to himself the reason for it, by considering the nature of the process of projection and section. The same remark applies to the observations that follow.

Two parallel lines in the original will not in general be represented by parallel lines in the picture; equal distances in the original do not in general correspond to equal distances in the picture; the perspective representation of a circle is usually an ellipse; etc.

It is clear then that the perspective representation of an object involves a very considerable distortion, but always such that points are represented by points and straight lines by straight lines (except when a line of the original figure passes through O).

The attentive reader will have noted, however, that the process described above, of representing a given three-dimensional figure on a plane does not in general establish a *reciprocally* one-to-one correspondence between the points of the given figure and those of the plane. For if two points of the former are on a line with O, they correspond to the same point on the latter, and if two lines of the former are on the same plane through O, they correspond to the same line of the latter. The process of projection and section does, however, in general give rise to a reciprocally one-to-one correspondence, *if the elements of the first figure all lie in one plane.* Such a correspondence is more precisely defined in the next section. It is illustrated in a photograph, if attention is confined to one plane of the scene depicted.

3. Projective transformations. Let F be any figure in a plane and let it be projected from a point O not in the plane of the figure. The section of the projection by a plane gives rise to a new figure F' and the correspondence between the elements of F and F' is called a *perspective correspondence* or a *perspective transformation.* If then F' be projected from a new center O' on to a third plane a new figure F'' results. The figure F'' is obtained from F by means of two perspective transformations, one performed after the other. Similarly, we may consider the result of a sequence of any number of perspective correspondences. This leads to the following definition:

The resultant of a sequence of perspective transformations is called a *projective transformation* or a *projective correspondence.*

The concept of a projective correspondence lies at the very foundation of projective geometry, as will be seen in what follows. Indeed, we may now characterize projective geometry as follows: *Projective geometry is concerned with those properties of figures which remain unchanged by projective transformations.*

It follows at once that the parallelism of straight lines, the equality of distances or of angles, can have no place in projective geometry, since these properties are all changed by projective transformations. Parallel lines may be transformed into intersecting lines, equal distances may be transformed into unequal distances, right angles may be transformed into acute or obtuse angles, etc. On the other hand, a point and a straight line are always transformed into a point and a straight line respectively by any projective transformation (no matter how many projections and sections may have had a part in the projective transformation); also, if a point A of F is on a line l of F, the point A' corresponding to A under any projective transformation will lie on the line l' corresponding to l; and if A is not on l, A' will not be on l'. Two intersecting straight lines will correspond to two intersecting straight lines, a triangle will correspond to a triangle, a quadrilateral to a quadrilateral, etc. Certain possible exceptions to some of the above statements which may occur to the critical reader will, as has been indicated, be considered presently. Enough has been said to show that properties concerning merely the *incidence* of points and lines are *projective properties*, i.e., properties which remain unchanged under projective transformations, while any properties concerned with measurement, i.e., *metric properties*, are foreign to projective geometry as such. We shall see later, however, how such metric properties may be obtained from projective properties by a process of specialization.

A triangle is, as has been indicated, a figure of projective geometry; but equilateral, or isosceles, or right triangles are not; because they involve properties which are not preserved under projective transformations. A quadrilateral is a figure of projective geometry; but a parallelogram, a rectangle, a square, etc. is not. It will be seen later that a conic section is a curve of projective geometry, but that the classification into hyperbola, ellipse, and parabola involves metric properties.

At first sight it may appear that the consideration of projective properties only would so greatly restrict the field of operations as to give little content to projective geometry. This, however, is not the case, as will soon become apparent enough. By confining ourselves to the consideration of projective properties the resulting geometry becomes structurally much simpler than one involving in addition a host of metric properties; but projective geometry is, nevertheless, very rich in content. Indeed, as has already been indicated, it contains, when its theorems are suitably specialized, the whole content of ordinary euclidean metric geometry and also the content of certain non-euclidean geometries. Such considerations, which will mean much more to the uninitiated reader when he has reached the end of this monograph than they can possibly mean now, led the English mathematician Cayley to exclaim: "Projective Geometry is all geometry." To make clear in what sense this famous dictum is true is one of the primary objects of this little book.

4. A projective theorem. The reader who is approaching the study of projective geometry for the

first time will be curious as to the nature of a geometric theorem which involves no metric conceptions. The following proposition, known as Desargues' Theorem on perspective triangles, will prove to be fundamental in the systematic development of certain parts of projective geometry to which the later chapters are devoted:

If two triangles ABC and A'B'C' are so related that the three points of intersection of the pairs of sides AB and A'B', BC and B'C', CA and C'A' are on a straight line, the lines AA', BB', CC' joining corresponding vertices all pass through the same point (or are parallel). (The phrase in parentheses is necessary as long as we state the theorem in the so-called metric space of ordinary geometry; it becomes unnecessary in the projective space to be introduced in the next chapter, in which the theorem will, moreover, gain in content.)

It will be observed that we have here a theorem which involves in its statement only the incidence of points and lines; no metric notions are involved. A formal proof of the theorem will be given later (p. 34). At this point it is a good exercise for the spatial imagination to observe that, if the two triangles are in different planes, the theorem is almost self-evident. If the reader will exercise his imagination sufficiently to get a clear mental picture of two intersecting planes, in each of which is a triangle whose pairs of corresponding sides intersect on a line (the latter must be the intersection of the two planes), the conclusion of the theorem follows almost immediately. In fact, every pair of the lines AA', BB', CC' lies in a plane, and three planes must intersect in a point (or in parallel lines or in a single line). The reader may then think of one of the planes as rotating about its line of intersection with the other plane until it comes to coincide with the latter. This will make the theorem appear plausible, at least, even for the case when the two triangles are in the same plane.

Although the historical origin of projective geometry goes back to the latter part of the fifteenth century, and although isolated theorems of this form of geometry were proved by Desargues (1593–1662) and Pascal (1623–1662), projective geometry as a self-contained discipline was not developed until the great French mathematician Poncelet (1788–1867) published his classic "Traité des propriétés projectives des figures" in 1822. Since then the development of this branch of geometry has been rapid, so that it is now recognized as one of the truly fundamental disciplines of modern mathematics, not only on account of its varied and important contacts with mathematics as a whole, but also on account of the intrinsic beauty of its structure and of its results.

This beauty is largely due to its simplicity. The latter is due not merely to stripping geometry of the complexities of its various metric concepts, but in no small measure also to the introduction of a new conception of space. To describe this "projective" space is the object of the next chapter, after which we may begin the more systematic development of our subject to the extent that the small compass of this monograph will permit.

References. Besides the classic treatise of Poncelet already referred to, the reader interested in the historical development of the subject may consult Chasles,

Aperçu historique sur l'origine et le développement des méthodes en géométrie, Paris, 1837; also, various parts of the *Source Book in Mathematics*, edited by David Eugene Smith, New York, 1929.

CHAPTER II

PROJECTIVE SPACE. THE PRINCIPLE OF DUALITY

5. Ideal elements. We had occasion in the preceding chapter to refer to the fact that the "one-to-one" character of a perspective correspondence is, in metric space, subject to certain exceptions. Our first task in the present chapter must be to examine these exceptions and to see how to remove them.

If the process of projection and section, described in the last chapter for three-dimensional space, is confined to a single plane, we obtain the idea of a perspective correspondence between the points of two lines in a plane. If u and u' in the adjoining figure are two such lines (in the future we use the word line always to mean straight line, unless otherwise specified), and if S is any point in the plane of the two lines, but not on either line, the lines joining S to points A, B, C, $\cdots$ of u will in general meet u' in definite points A', B', C', $\cdots$. To any point of u, say A, will correspond by means of this construction a uniquely determined point A'; to B will correspond B'; to C, C'; and so on. Vice-versa to every point of u' corresponds, in general, a uniquely determined point of u. The point of inter-

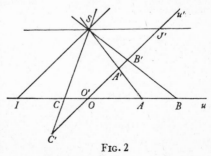

FIG. 2

11

section $O = O'$ of the two lines obviously corresponds to itself. A correspondence defined by the process just described is called a *perspective correspondence* between the points of u and u'; the point S is called the *center of perspectivity*. We also say that the points of u(or u') are *projected* into the points of u' (or u) *from the center S*.

From what has just been said the perspective correspondence thus defined is, in general, reciprocally one-to-one. However, the point I on u in which the line through S parallel to u' meets u has in our present metric conception of the plane no corresponding point on u'. Also, the point J' on u' in which the line through S parallel to u meets u' is not the correspondent of any point on u. In order to avoid this exception we conceive of an additional point on each of the lines, a point I' on u' to correspond to I, and a point J on u to be the correspondent of J'. If for the time being we call the points of our familiar metric plane "ordinary" points, such new points as I' and J must be regarded as "ideal" points which are to be thought of as arbitrarily added to the plane for a definite purpose. One such ideal point is thought of as existing on every line; any set of parallel lines are all thought of as containing the same ideal point. An "ideal point" is also called a "point at infinity."

At first this may strike the reader as a very mystifying performance. However, he will soon become familiar with the new conception. The following remarks will, it is hoped, assist him in this direction. Two intersecting lines have a point in common. Two parallel lines also have something in common, namely their direction. If we choose to use the phrase "ideal point of a line" instead of the words "direction of a line" it will be found that the new terminology is equally intelligible. For example: A straight line is uniquely determined by one of its points and its direction (old terminology); a straight line is uniquely determined by one of its ordinary points and its ideal point (new terminology). The two statements mean exactly the same thing.

Two parallel lines have the same direction (old terminology);

Two parallel lines have the same ideal point (new terminology).

If two or more lines have the same direction, they are parallel (O.T.);

If two or more lines have the same ideal point, they are parallel (N.T.).

If, then, we think of every straight line as containing in addition to all of its ordinary points one ideal point, we get the conception of a *projective line*, as soon as we drop the distinction between ordinary and ideal, and regard all the points, ideal as well as ordinary, as being in every way equivalent. We can now see why it is that projective geometry as such can not consider parallelism. In projective geometry every two straight lines in the same plane have a point in common, i.e., intersect. All points being regarded as equivalent, it can make no difference in a projective theorem whether this point of intersection is ideal or ordinary.

The set of all ideal points of a plane is thought of as constituting a straight line, the so-called *ideal line*, or the *line at infinity*. One such ideal line is thought of as existing in every plane. A reason for this conception lies in the fact that every ordinary straight line in a plane has one and only one point in common with the set of all ideal points in the plane, and "to be met by a straight line in one and only one point" is characteristic of a straight line.

6. The projective plane. This completes the description of a projective plane. To repeat, *a projective plane consists of all the ordinary points and straight lines of a metric plane and, in addition, of a set of ideal points all of which are supposed to line on one ideal line and such that one such ideal point lies on every ordinary line.*

In such a projective plane a perspective correspondence, as previously defined, between the points of two lines is reciprocally one-to-one throughout *without exception*. The point I' on u' corresponding to I on u is the ideal point of u'; the point J of u which is the correspondent of the point J' of u' is the ideal point of u.

As another consequence of the conception of a projective plane we may note that we are led by this conception to think of the projective straight line as *closed*, like a circle of huge radius. Given a straight line u and a center of perspectivity S, let us think of a variable line through S as rotating from the position SA

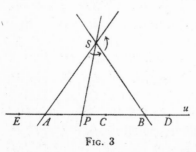

Fig. 3

to the position SB in the direction indicated by the arrow in the adjoining figure. The variable line meets u in a variable point P which under the continuous rotation specified moves continuously from A to B, describing the segment ACB. As the variable line continues to rotate from the position SB in the same direction as before to its original position, the variable point P in which this line meets u traces out all the rest of the line continuously, so that the remainder of the line $BDEA$ must be thought of as constituting a continuous segment just like ACB. Two distinct points A and B of a projective line divide it into two segments, just as two distinct points on a circle divide the latter into two segments. The two parts BD and EA are to be thought of as joined together, as it were, by the ideal point on u. The difficulty of forming a mental picture of how this happens should not disturb the reader. He is in this respect no better off in his familiar conception of the metric plane. In the latter he is expected to imagine that the variable point of intersection P of the rotating line with u suddenly ceases to exist for a moment (when the rotating line is parallel with u) only to materialize again at the other end of the line an instant later. It is just as difficult to form a mental picture of how this can happen as it is to imagine the process implied by the projective conception. The proper mental attitude to take is simply not to attempt to form a mental picture of a closed straight line; but to accept the fact that the projective line behaves *as though it were closed*.

The situation to be grasped will become more vivid to the reader, if he notes that an apparently broken segment like $BDEA$ in the adjoining figure may be perspective with an ordinary closed segment $B'D'E'A'$. This fact is at once apparent from Fig. 4. If a line through S rotates continuously from the position SB to the position $SA' = SA$ in the direction of the arrow, the point of intersection of the rotating line with u

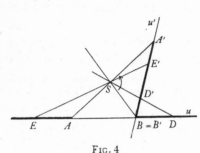

FIG. 4

moves from B over D to E and thence to A, while the corresponding point on u' moves from $B'(=B)$ over D' and E' to A'. The corresponding segments have been drawn more heavily in the figure in order to exhibit more clearly the corresponding parts.

These considerations show, moreover, that on a projective line three points are necessary to determine a segment on the line or a direction on the line. To give merely the end points A and B of a segment would leave us in doubt as to which of two segments is meant; and the direction AB might mean either of the two directions indicated by the arrows in the adjoining figure. If, however, we specify the segment ACB or the direction ACB the segment or the direction is

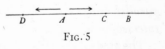

FIG. 5

uniquely determined; similarly for the segment ADB or the direction ADB.

Before proceeding to build up in a similar manner the conception of a projective space of three dimensions, it may be well to consider briefly some of the advantages that accrue from the conception of a projective plane.

In the statement of Desargues' theorem in the preceding chapter (p. 8) we found it necessary to add a phrase in parentheses to take account of the possibility that the three lines joining the corresponding vertices AA', BB', CC' of the triangle might be parallel instead of intersecting in a point. This was because we there stated the theorem for the metric plane. We see now that the parenthetical phrase is quite unnecessary (and, indeed, meaningless) if the theorem is interpreted as applying to two triangles in a projective plane, since parallel lines in a metric plane are lines intersecting in an (ideal) point in a projective plane. We remarked in the same connection that this theorem would gain in content under the conception of a projective plane. This is because various metric specializations of the hypothesis of the theorem lead to different metric theorems. For example:

If a pair of sides of two triangles are parallel to the line joining the intersections of two other pairs of sides, the lines joining corresponding vertices will intersect in a single point or be parallel. Or, again:

If the three pairs of sides of two triangles consist of parallel lines, the lines joining corresponding vertices intersect in a single point or are parallel.

The first of these specializations results from assuming that one of the points of intersection of corresponding sides is an ideal point; the second, from the assumption that two (and hence all three) of such points of intersection are ideal. The reader here gets an illustration of how a single projective theorem may give rise to several metric theorems through appropriate specialization.

An advantage of far-reaching importance accrues from the symmetry existing between point and line in a projective plane. Consider the following two propositions of plane geometry:

Any two distinct points determine one and only one line on which they both lie.

Any two distinct lines determine one and only one point through which they both pass.

The first of these propositions is true in the metric plane without exception. The second, however, has an exception in the metric plane, if the two lines are parallel. In the projective plane, on the other hand, both propositions are valid without exception. If, in the second, the lines are parallel, they still determine one and only one (ideal) point through which they both pass. If one of the lines is ideal, the proposition still holds. Both lines cannot be ideal, since they are distinct. In the first proposition we need only consider the cases where one of the given points is ideal and where both are ideal. In each of these cases the proposition is at once seen to be valid.

If now we consider the relation between the statements of these two propositions, we see that by simply interchanging the words "point" and "line" in one of them we obtain the other, except for the fact that the last phrase of the theorem will after the interchange sound peculiar. In case we make this interchange in the first proposition, we obtain: Any two distinct lines determine one and only one point on which they both lie. The fact that the last phrase sounds peculiar to us is, however, due to a blemish in our language. For, the relation of a point lying on a line and that of a line passing through a point are precisely the same. A perfect language would express two such identical relations in the same words. For example, we might agree to express this relation by either of the forms: a point is *on* a line or a line is *on* a point. If we adopt this modification of our language, which it should be noted is perfectly intelligible even though the second form sounds queer, the two propositions above are obtained, either one from the other, by a mere mechanical interchange of the words "point" and "line":

Two distinct points are on one and only one line.	*Two distinct lines are on one and only one point.*

This modification of our language we will in the future, when we have occasion to use it, refer to as the "on" language.

On the symmetry thus noted between the roles played by point and line in plane geometry depends one of the most far-reaching principles of modern mathematics, the so-called "principle of duality." According to this principle all the propositions of plane projective geometry occur in such dual pairs; in other words, from any proposition of plane projective geometry another proposition can be inferred in which the roles played by the words point and line are interchanged. This principle is a special case of the so-called principle of duality in space. We shall have more to say of it after we have considered the fundamental properties of projective space, to which we now turn our attention.

7. **Projective space.** The introduction of the concept of ideal points and that of the ideal line in a plane has prepared us, no doubt, for the introduction of ideal elements in three dimensional space. We can, therefore,

describe the latter more briefly than would otherwise be the case. If we consider the perspective correspondence between the two planes π and π' established by projection from a center S not in either plane, whereby to any point A of π corresponds the point A' of π' in which the line SA meets π', we observe that any point I of π such that the line SI is parallel to π' has

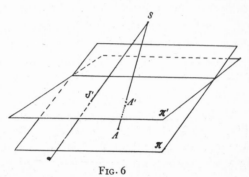

Fig. 6

(in metric space) no corresponding point I' in π'. All the lines SI parallel to π' lie in the plane through S parallel to π'. This plane cuts π in a line i. Corresponding to all the points of this line i we introduce in π' ideal points I', which constitute by definition the ideal line I' of π'. Similarly, the plane through S parallel to π meets π' in a line j', corresponding to which we introduce an ideal line j on π, which contains all the points J corresponding to the points J' of j'. Our perspective correspondence is now reciprocally one-to-one without exception.

It will be observed that we are thus led to precisely the same conception of a projective plane to which the earlier consideration of a perspective correspondence in a single plane led us. We are thereby brought naturally to the conception that every plane in projective space is to be such a projective plane, obtained from a metric plane by the addition of ideal points which all lie on a single ideal line. All that is needed to complete the conception of projective space is to add that all the ideal points and all the ideal lines are to be thought of as lying in the same *ideal plane*. In other words, *projective three-dimensional space* is obtained from metric three-dimensional space by adding to the latter the points and lines of an ideal plane, one such ideal point lying on every ordinary line, one such ideal line lying on every ordinary plane. Any set of parallel lines in space have the same ideal point in common; any set of parallel planes have the same ideal line in common.

We are now in a position to gain a clear understanding of the fundamental properties of the incidence of points, lines, and planes in projective space. We will state them in pairs for the purpose of exhibiting the duality which we will discuss a little later.

1. *Any two distinct points determine one and only one line on which they both lie.*

1'. *Any two distinct planes determine one and only one line through which they both pass.*

The reader should not fail to make clear to himself just how these propositions express relations with which he is already familiar from his study of ordinary metric geometry, taking account of the various possible special cases involving parallelism which are taken care of by the ideal elements introduced to form projective space. Thus, for example, 1' contains the familiar proposition of solid geometry that any two non-parallel planes intersect in a straight line. It contains further the conception that any two parallel planes pass through the same ideal line; and that an ordinary plane and the ideal plane have a line in common. Proposition 1, on the other hand, in addition to the proposition that two distinct ordinary points determine a line, contains the conception that an ordinary point and an ideal point determine a line; and also, that two distinct ideal points determine an ideal line.

2. *Three points, which are not on the same line, determine one and only one plane on which they all lie.*

2'. *Three planes, which do not pass through the same line, determine one and only one point through which they all pass.*

Here, in 2', if no two of the three planes are parallel, the proposition is a well-known theorem of solid geometry, provided the planes do not intersect in parallel lines; if they do intersect in parallel lines, the proposition is still valid, the point determined by them being ideal. If two of the planes are parallel and the third intersects them in ordinary lines, the latter are parallel and determine uniquely an ideal point common to the three planes. If all three planes are parallel, they all pass through the same ideal line and hence do not satisfy the restriction of the theorem. Other special cases could be listed; but the reader should note them for himself, and observe in each case that the proposition is valid. He should treat proposition 2 in the same way, considering the cases where all three of the given points are ordinary, where two are ordinary and one is ideal, where one is ordinary and two are ideal, and where all three are ideal. The reader should analyze each of the following propositions in the same way. He will then secure very quickly a thorough grasp of the fundamental properties of incidence in projective space.

3. *A point and a line not containing the point determine one and only plane on which they both lie.*

3'. *A plane and a line not on the plane determine one and only one point through which they both pass.*

4. *Any two distinct lines in the same plane intersect in one and only one point.*

4'. *Any two distinct lines having a point in common determine one and only one plane.*

The reader has probably already noted the fact that in each of the pairs of propositions 1 and 1', 2 and 2', etc., one of the pair may be obtained from the other by interchanging the roles of "point" and "plane," leaving "line" unchanged. As previously noted for propositions in a plane (where the duality was between point and line) this interchange could be a mere mechanical transposition of the words point and plane were it not for an imperfection of our language. The "on" language already described for the plane may, however, be extended to space. We say a point is on a plane; we may describe this relation equally well by saying that *the plane is on the point,* instead of using one of the more familiar phrases that the plane passes through or contains the point. If a line is on a plane, we may say also that the plane is on the line; etc.

If, now, the propositions 1 and 1', 2 and 2', etc. are all stated in the "on" language, it will be found that one proposition of each pair goes over into the other by a mere mechanical interchange of the words "point" and "plane," the word "line" being left unchanged. For example, Proposition 4 stated in the "on" language would read as follows: *Any two distinct lines on the same plane are on one and only one common point.* If in this proposition we interchange the words point and plane we obtain: *Any two distinct lines on the same point are on one and only one common plane.* This is evidently the same as Proposition 4'. The reader should restate each of the other propositions (1, 2, 3) in the "on" language and verify the fact that the mere mechanical interchange of the words point and plane produces the dual propositions (1', 2', 3').

8. The principle of duality. The pairs of propositions 1 and 1', 2 and 2', etc. are all examples of what are known as *pairs of dual propositions*, each one of a pair being the (space) *dual* of the other. The general principle of which these pairs are special instances is known as the Principle of Duality in Space. It may be stated as follows:

THE PRINCIPLE OF DUALITY IN SPACE. *If any projective theorem regarding points, lines, and planes in space is stated in the "on" language, a second theorem may be obtained from it by simply interchanging the words point and plane.*

This principle is one of the most important and beautiful principles in the whole field of modern geometry. It means that we need give the proof of only one of two dual theorems, the other being necessarily valid without further proof, assuming of course that the principle of duality has been established. It exhibits at one stroke a symmetry in the structure of projective geometry which can not fail to be impressive. It did not appear explicitly until near the beginning of the nineteenth century. It was first stated by Gergonne in 1826, but was led up to by the writings of Poncelet and others during the first quarter of the century. It is, therefore, a very modern theorem. The reader will be impressed by its far-reaching character as we proceed.

The proof of the principle of duality may be made in various ways. It is possible to give a complete set of postulates for projective geometry which are themselves arranged in dual pairs. Any theorem derived formally from such a set of postulates may then obviously be dualized by simply dualizing each step in the proof. In such a brief and elementary treatment of projective geometry as the present, however, it does not seem desirable to give the space necessary for a postulational treatment. The reader may, if he is interested in this method of proof, consult Veblen and Young, *Projective Geometry*, Vol. I, Chapter I.

The principle may also be proved analytically without difficulty, once the analytic machinery appropriate to projective geometry has been built (See Chapter VI of the present monograph). Finally, the principle of duality follows readily from the group of theorems which concern the fundamental relations of poles and polars with respect to a conic (p. 80), which will be proved later. The reader is, therefore, requested to accept the principle of duality on faith for the time being. We propose to make free use of the principle from now on, recognizing that in any given case we can always prove the dual theorem, if we wish, by dualizing the proof of the original theorem.

A corollary to the principle of duality in space is the corresponding principle in the plane, which is as follows:

THE PRINCIPLE OF DUALITY IN THE PLANE. *If any projective theorem concerning points and lines of a plane is stated in the "on" language, a second theorem is obtained from it by interchanging the words point and line.*

This principle may be derived from the principle of duality in space as follows: Let F be any figure consisting of points and lines in a plane and let O be any point not on this plane. The projection from O of the figure F then consists of a set, F', of lines and planes through O, such that whenever a point of F lies on a line of F, the corresponding line of F' will lie in the corresponding plane of F'. The space dual of F' will then consist of *a set, F'', of lines and points on a plane* (this italicized phrase being the dual of the phrase "a set of lines and planes through a point"). The principle of duality in a plane now follows almost immediately by considering the relation between the two plane figures F and F''. To every point P of F corresponds a line OP of F' and to the latter line corresponds a line of F''; to every line l of F corresponds a plane through O and l of F' and to this plane of F' corresponds a point of F''. Moreover, if the point P lies on the line l, the line corresponding to P in F'' will pass through the point corresponding to l. To any projective property of F will then correspond a projective property of F'' obtained from the former by interchanging the rôles of point and line.

9. Elementary figures. We are now ready to begin a more systematic study of projective properties of figures. In the interest of simplicity we shall confine ourselves largely to figures in a plane, although we shall find it desirable occasionally, as for example in our proof of Desargues' theorem at the beginning of the next chapter, to make use of three-dimensional figures. We will close the present chapter with the definitions of certain elementary figures of projective geometry. As might be expected these figures occur, in general, in dual pairs.

If three or more points are on the same line, the points are said to be *collinear*.	If three or more lines pass through the same point, the lines are said to be *concurrent*.

The figure consisting of three non-collinear points and the three lines joining them in pairs is called a *triangle*. The points are called the *vertices* and the lines are called the *sides* of the triangle.

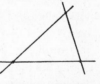

FIG. 7. *Triangle*

A triangle is a self-dual figure in the plane. For the dual of the definition just given is evidently: "The figure consisting of three non-concurrent lines and their three points of intersection by pairs is called a triangle." It should be noted that the conception of a triangle in projective geometry differs from the corresponding

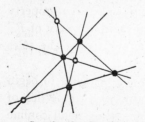

Complete Quadrangle

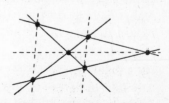

Complete Quadrilateral

FIG. 8

conception in metric geometry, since in the latter the side of a triangle consists only of the segment of the line between two vertices, while in projective geometry it consists of the whole line (see Fig. 7).

The figure consisting of four points in a plane (no three of which are collinear) together with the six lines joining pairs of these points is called a *complete quadrangle*. The four points are called the *vertices* (marked ●) and the six lines are called the *sides* of the quadrangle. Two sides which do not have a vertex in common are said to be *opposite*. The intersections of the three pairs of opposite sides are called *diagonal points* (marked ○ in Fig. 8 left).

If the points of two figures (in the same plane) correspond in such a way that the lines joining every pair of corresponding points are concurrent in a point O, the figures are said to be *perspective* from the *center O*.

The figure consisting of four lines in a plane (no three of which are concurrent) together with the six points in which pairs of these lines intersect is called a *complete quadrilateral*. The four lines are called the *sides* and the six points are called the *vertices* of the quadrilateral. Two vertices not on the same side are said to be *opposite*. The lines joining the three pairs of opposite vertices are called *diagonal lines* (dotted in Fig. 8 right).

If the lines of two figures (in the same plane) correspond in such a way that the points of intersection of every pair of corresponding lines are collinear on a line l, the figures are said to be *perspective* from the *axis l*.

With a *central perspectivity* as defined on the left we have already become familiar. The idea of an *axial perspectivity* defined on the right is, however, new. It is a good illustration of how the concepts of projective geometry occur in dual pairs throughout. We give next our first definition of a three-dimensional figure.

The figure consisting of four points not all in the same plane, together with the four planes joining them in threes and the six lines joining them in pairs, is called a *tetrahedron*. The four points, six lines, and four planes are called the *vertices*, *edges*, and *faces* of the tetrahedron, respectively.

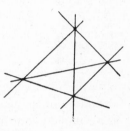

FIG. 9. *Tetrahedron*

The tetrahedron is a self-dual figure in space. Let the reader dualize the above definition in space and convince himself of the truth of this assertion. He should indeed take every opportunity to dualize both in the plane and in space, in order that he may become thoroughly familiar with the process. If he does so it will not be long before he will dualize with ease, even though at first it may require some effort of concentration and analysis. The following space figure will be used at the beginning of the next chapter:

The figure consisting of five points, no four of which are in the same plane, together with the ten lines joining them in pairs and the ten planes joining every three of them, is called a *complete five-point in space*.

The reader should note the general principle which

has governed the definition of the figures thus far defined. In the last, the figure consists of five points, no four of which are in the same plane, and of *all* the lines and planes joining them. Since every pair of distinct points determines a line and since the number of combinations of five things taken two at a time is $5 \cdot 4/2 = 10$, there are ten lines in our figure; and, since every three non-collinear points determine a plane (and no three of our points can be collinear, in view of the fact that no four are in the same plane) and the number of combinations of five things taken three at a time is $5 \cdot 4 \cdot 3/3!$ $= 10$, there must be ten planes in our figure. This principle is reflected by the adjective "complete" in the definition of complete five-point. Thus the tetrahedron is a complete four-point in space; the triangle is a complete three-point in a plane, the complete quadrangle is a complete four-point in a plane, the complete quadrilateral is a complete four-line in a plane, etc. It should be clear now what is meant by a complete *n*-point in a plane or in space, etc.

A *simple quadrangle*, on the other hand, consists of four points A, B, C, D, (no three of which are collinear) in a given cyclical order $ABCD$ together with the four lines joining successive pairs of these points (AB, BC, CD, DA).

The complete space five-point is not self-dual. Its dual in space is the so-called *complete five-plane*, consisting of five planes, ten lines, and ten points. We shall not have occasion, however, to use the latter figure.

CHAPTER III

10. The Desargues configuration. We begin our more systematic study of projective geometry by considering the section of a complete space five-point by a plane not passing through any of the vertices. Since the

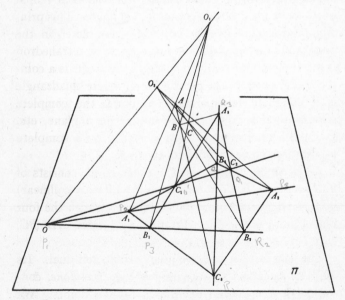

FIG. 10

five-point consists, in addition to its five vertices, of ten lines and ten planes, the plane section to be considered will be a plane figure consisting of ten points

and ten lines. In order to gain more readily a clear
conception of the mutual relations of these points and
lines we will consider the five-point as made up of a
triangle ABC and two other points O_1, O_2, together with
the lines and planes joining these points in pairs and
triples. The projection from O_1 of the triangle ABC
on the plane of section π is a triangle $A_1B_1C_1$; similarly,
the projection of ABC from O_2 gives in π a triangle
$A_2B_2C_2$. The line O_1O_2 meets π in a point O, and the
planes O_1O_2A, O_1O_2B, O_1O_2C meet π in three lines
passing through O and containing the pairs of points
A_1A_2, B_1B_2, C_1C_2, respectively. The plane section of
our complete five-point may, therefore, be described
as consisting, in part, of two triangles $A_1B_1C_1$ and
$A_2B_2C_2$, such that the lines A_1A_2, B_1B_2, C_1C_2 are concurrent in O. This description accounts for seven of the
ten points and for nine of the ten lines in the plane section of our five-point. The remaining line is clearly the
line in which the plane ABC meets π, and the three
remaining points are the points A_3, B_3, C_3 in which the
lines BC, CA, AB, respectively, meet π. The three
points A_3, B_3, C_3 are evidently on the line in which the
plane ABC meets π. On the other hand, A_3 is the
intersection of the lines B_1C_1 and B_2C_2, since the latter
lines are in the planes, O_1BC and O_2BC, respectively.
The plane section of a complete space five-point may
then be described as consisting of two triangles $A_1B_1C_1$
and $A_2B_2C_2$, perspective from a point O, and whose
pairs of corresponding sides intersect in collinear points
A_3, B_3, C_3.

This figure is known as the *Desargues configuration*.
A *plane configuration*, in general, is a figure consisting

of a_{11} points and a_{22} lines such that through each of the points pass the same number a_{12} of the lines of the figure and such that on each line lie the same number a_{21} of the points of the figure. The symbol $\left(\begin{smallmatrix} a_{11}, & a_{21} \\ a_{12}, & a_{22} \end{smallmatrix}\right)$ is then associated with such a configuration. It may be noted that the Desargues configuration has the symbol $\left(\begin{smallmatrix} 10, & 3 \\ 3, & 10 \end{smallmatrix}\right)$, since it consists of ten points and ten lines such that three of the lines pass through each of the points and three of the points lie on each of the lines. A triangle is a configuration whose symbol is $\left(\begin{smallmatrix} 3 & 2 \\ 2 & 3 \end{smallmatrix}\right)$; a quadrangle is a configuration whose symbol is $\left(\begin{smallmatrix} 4 & 2 \\ 3 & 6 \end{smallmatrix}\right)$; etc. We shall occasionally meet other configurations; but their systematic study, as such, is beyond the scope of a brief monograph.

We have described the Desargues configuration, unsymmetrically, by assigning a special rôle to one of its points, namely O, i.e., by assigning a special rôle to one line O_1O_2 of the five-point. This line might, however, equally well have been any one of the nine other lines of the five-point. The Desargues configuration is completely symmetrical as to its points and lines. It may be considered in ten different ways as consisting of two triangles perspective from a point, each of the ten points of the configuration in turn being considered the center of perspectivity. The reader should, in the figure, choose several points as centers of perspectivity and pick out the corresponding pair of perspective triangles, observing in each case that the pairs of corresponding sides meet in three points lying on à line of the figure.

We may now give a proof of the Theorem of Desargues, which we cited for illustrative purposes in

Chapter I (p. 8). We will state it in the following brief form, which is justified on the basis of a definition of perspectivity from a line which we gave in the last chapter (p. 29).

THE THEOREM OF DESARGUES. *If two triangles are perspective from a point, they are perspective from a line; and conversely.*

After the preceding discussion of the Desargues configuration, in order to prove the theorem, we need only show that any pair of triangles $A_1B_1C_1$ and $A_2B_2C_2$, which are perspective from a point O, may be considered as part of a plane section of a complete space five-point. We may consider the two triangles as lying in the same plane, since the theorem is directly evident, if they lie in different planes (p. 8). Let O_1, O_2 be any two distinct points collinear with O and not in the plane of the triangles. Since A_1A_2 passes through O, by hypothesis, the points O_1, O_2, A_1, A_2 all lie in the same plane. The lines O_1A_1 and O_2A_2 will therefore intersect in a point A. Similarly, the lines O_1B_1 and O_2B_2 intersect in a point B; and the lines O_1C_1 and O_2C_2 in a point C. The points O_1, O_2, A, B, C are the vertices of a complete five point of which the two given perspective triangles are part of a plane section. They are, then, part of a Desargues configuration, and their pairs of corresponding sides must intersect in collinear points; i.e., they are perspective from a line.

The converse of the theorem (if two triangles are perspective from a line, they are perspective from a point) is the plane dual of the original theorem, if the triangles are in the same plane, and does not therefore require a separate proof, if the principle of duality be accepted. The reader will find no difficulty, however, in giving a proof of the converse along the lines indicated for the direct theorem.

11. The fundamental theorem on quadrangular sets. As an application of the theorem of Desargues, we will now prove the following important theorem:

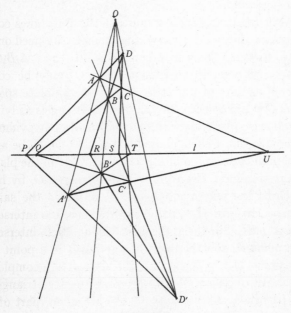

FIG. 11

If two complete quadrangles ABCD and A'B'C'D' correspond—A to A', B to B', etc.,—in such a way that five of the pairs of corresponding sides intersect on a line l, the sixth pair of corresponding sides will also intersect on l.

To prove this, let P, Q, R, S, T be the five points in

which the five pairs of corresponding sides of the quadrangles meet l by hypothesis. The triangles BCD and
$B'C'D'$, having their three sides meeting l in Q, R, S,
respectively, are perspective from a point (Theorem of
Desargues). Similarly, the triangles ABD and $A'B'D'$
are perspective from a point. Moreover, the center of
perspectivity is the same for both these pairs of triangles, being the intersection of BB' and DD'. The
two quadrangles are, therefore, perspective from O;
in particular, the triangles ABC and $A'B'C'$ are perspective from O. Their pairs of corresponding sides,
therefore, intersect in collinear points Q, T, U. The
points Q and T being on l, U must also be on l.

The set of six (or five, or four) points in which the
sides of a complete quadrangle meet a line is called a
quadrangular set of points. The points of a quadrangular
set may reduce to five or four if the line l passes through
one or two of the diagonal points of the quadrangle.

A quadrangular set cannot consist of less than four
points, since, in the space we are considering, *the three
diagonal points of a complete quadrangle are never collinear*.

12. Harmonic sets. Of special importance is the case
where the line l contains two of the diagonal points

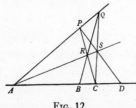

Fig. 12

(p. 28) of the quadrangle. If
A and C are two diagonal
points of the quadrangle $PQRS$
and B and D are the points in
which the remaining two sides
of the quadrangle meet AC, the
set of points AC, BD is called a
harmonic set of points and is indicated by the symbol

$H(AC, BD)$. The points BD are said to be *harmonic* with respect to A and C; also D (or B) is called the *harmonic conjugate* of B (or D) with respect to A and C; in symbols, $D = H(AC, B)$, $B = H(AC, D)$. By the preceding theorem, D is uniquely determined as soon as A, C, and B are given. Hence we have the theorem:

The harmonic conjugate of a point with respect to two others is uniquely determined.

Further, *if B, D are harmonic with respect to A and C, then A, C are harmonic with respect to B and D.* In the figure, let the harmonic set $H(AC, BD)$ be determined by the quadrangle $PQRS$, with diagonal points at A

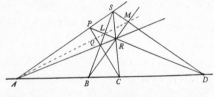

Fig. 13

and C. We wish to show that then B and D are diagonal points of a complete quadrangle the remaining two sides of which pass through A and C. To this end, draw BR and DS meeting in M; let L be the intersection of PR and QS. The triangles PLQ and SMR are then perspective from the line BD. The line LM, therefore, passes through A (p. 34). The quadrangle $SMLR$ now satisfies the desired conditions: B and D are diagonal points, while C and A are on the remaining two sides of this quadrangle.

This establishes the fact that the pairs A, C and B, D in a harmonic set are interchangeable; in other words, *from the relation $H(AC, BD)$ follow the relations*

$H(AC, DB)$, $H(CA, BD)$, $H(CA, DB)$, $H(BD, AC)$, $H(BD, CA)$, $H(DB, AC)$, and $H(DB, CA)$.

The plane dual of a harmonic set of points is called a *harmonic set of lines*. It obviously consists of two pairs of coplanar lines a, c and b, d passing through the same point, such that a and c are diagonal lines of a complete quadrilateral and such that b and d are the lines joining the remaining vertices of the quadrilateral to the intersection of a and c. By virtue of the principle of duality the theorems just derived for a harmonic set of points apply equally well to a harmonic set of lines.

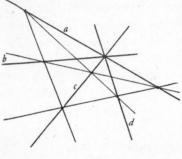

Fig. 14

Thus, *if a and c are harmonic with respect to b and d, b and d are harmonic with respect to a and c; the harmonic conjugate of a line b with respect to two others a and c (a, b, c being of course coplanar and concurrent) is a uniquely determined line; etc.*

The reason for the great importance which attaches to the idea of a harmonic set lies in the fact that such a set is, by any projective transformation, transformed into a harmonic set. We observed in the first chapter that projective geometry is concerned with those properties of figures which remain unchanged under projective transformations. Hitherto we have encountered only properties of alignment as projective properties; to these we may now add the harmonic property.

That this property is indeed invariant under any projective transformation follows at once from the following theorem:

The projection from any point of a harmonic set of points is a harmonic set of lines.

Let A, C and B, D be any harmonic set $H(AC, BD)$ and let O be any point not on the line AD. We wish to prove that the lines OA, OC and OB, OD constitute a harmonic set of lines. To this end draw a line through

A meeting OB, OC in P, Q, respectively; and draw CP meeting OA in R. The quadrangle $ORPQ$ has diagonal points at A and C and one of its sides passes through B. Since AC,

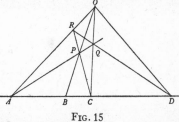

Fig. 15

BD form a harmonic set, the sixth side RQ passes through D. On the other hand, the lines AD, AQ; RD, RC form a quadrilateral, of which OA and OC are diagonal lines, while OB and OD pass through the remaining two vertices. The set of lines through O then form a harmonic set, by definition. This completes the proof.

The plane dual of the theorem just proved states that *the section by a line of a harmonic set of lines is a harmonic set of points.* It follows at once that by any sequence of projections and sections in a plane a harmonic set is always transformed into a harmonic set. Hence, we have the theroem:

Any set of lines or of points in a plane, which is projective with a harmonic set, is itself a harmonic set.

CHAPTER IV

PROJECTIVITIES IN ONE-DIMENSIONAL FORMS.
THE FUNDAMENTAL THEOREM

13. **The one-dimensional primitive forms in the plane.**
Before taking up a more detailed study of the projective transformations, we need the following definitions applying to *plane* figures:

The figure consisting of all the points on a line is called a *pencil of points* (or a *range*).	The figure consisting of all the lines through a point is called a *pencil of lines*.

All the lines of a pencil of lines are, it must be remembered, *in the same plane*. The set of all the lines in space passing through a given point is called a *bundle* of lines.

The pencil of points and the pencil of lines are the so-called *one-dimensional primitive forms in the plane*. (There is another one-dimensional primitive form in space, the so-called *pencil of planes*, which is the figure formed of all the planes through a given line.) We now propose to study in some detail the projective correspondences or transformations, more briefly, the *projectivities* between one-dimensional primitive forms in the plane. We recall first certain definitions:

A correspondence between the points of two pencils of points is said	A correspondence between the lines of two pencils of lines is said

to be *perspective*, if the lines joining the pairs of corresponding points are concurrent, i.e., if these lines form a pencil of lines.

to be *perspective*, if the points of intersection of pairs of corresponding lines are collinear, i.e., if these points form a pencil of points.

It will be observed that these definitions are equivalent to those previously given (p. 28); the terminology only is a little different. We need also the following:

A correspondence between a pencil of lines and a pencil of points is said to be *perspective*, if every line of the pencil of lines passes through the corresponding point of the pencil of points.

The symbol for a perspective correspondence, or a *perspectivity*, is $\overline{\wedge}$. The expression

$$ABCD \cdots \overset{S}{\overline{\wedge}} A'B'C'D' \cdots$$

indicates that the pencil of points A, B, C, D, $\cdots$ is perspective with the pencil A', B', C', D', $\cdots$ in such

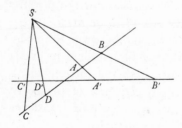

Fig. 16

a way that A corresponds to A', B to B', C to C', etc., and such that the lines AA', BB', CC', etc. all pass through S. The point S is called the *center* of the perspectivity, and the perspectivity is said to be *central*. (Fig. 16.) Likewise, the expression

$$abcd \cdots \overset{S}{\wedge} a'b'c'd' \cdots$$

indicates that the pencil of lines a, b, c, d, $\cdots$ is perspective with the pencil a', b', c', d', $\cdots$ in such a way that a corresponds to a', b to b', c to c', etc., and such

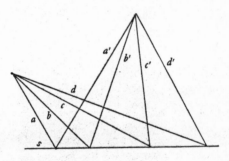

Fig. 17

that the points aa', bb', cc', etc. are all on the line s. The line s is called the *axis* of the perspectivity, and the perspectivity is said to be *axial*.

A correspondence between the elements (points or lines) of two one-dimensional primitive forms is said to be *projective*, if such a correspondence is effected by means of a finite sequence of perspectivities. Such a projective correspondence or transformation is called, more briefly, a *projectivity*.

Thus, for example, the figure (Fig. 18) shows the points of u perspective through S_1 with the points of u_1, the points of u_1 perspective through S_2 with the points of u_2, the points of u_2 perspective through S_3 with the points of u'. By this sequence of perspectivities every point of u is made to correspond to a uniquely determined point of u', namely, A to A', B to B', C to C', etc.

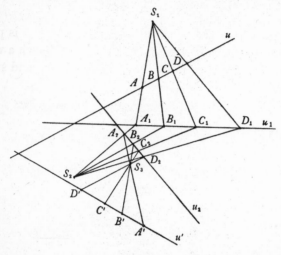

Fig. 18

The symbol for a projective correspondence is $\overline{\wedge}$. Thus the above correspondence would be indicated by

$$ABCD \cdots \overline{\wedge} A'B'C'D' \cdots .$$

It may be observed that the point of intersection of u and u' does not, in general, correspond to itself. In fact, we shall soon learn that, if it does correspond to itself in a projectivity, the latter is a perspectivity. In the example above a sequence of three perspectivities was used to define a projectivity; the number is immaterial, any number may be used. A perspectivity, it should be observed, is a special case of a projectivity.

14. Theorems on projectivities. The definition of a projectivity is very general. We propose now to prove a set of theorems which will culminate in the so-called *fundamental theorem of projective geometry*, whereby the apparent complexity of the concept will become much simplified.

Any three points on a line may be projected into any three points on another line by means of two centers of perspectivity.

To prove this, let A, B, C be any three points of a line u, and let A', B', C' be any three points of another line u'. We are to show that by means of two centers

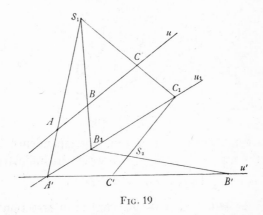

Fig. 19

of perspectivity we can project A into A', B into B', C into C'. If A concides with A' a single perspectivity is sufficient, since the intersection of BB' and CC' will serve as center from which to project A, B, C into A', B', C', respectively. If A and A' are distinct, draw the line AA' and let S_1 be any point on this line, distinct from A and A'. Draw any line u_1 (distinct from u')

through A' and project A, B, C from S_1 into A', B_1, C_1 on u_1. If, then, S_2 is the intersection of B_1B' and C_1C', we have

$$ABC \underset{\wedge}{\overset{S_1}{}} A'B_1C_1 \underset{\wedge}{\overset{S_2}{}} A'B'C'.$$

Therefore,

$$ABC \underset{\wedge}{\overline{}} A'B'C',$$

which proves our theorem. As an immediate corollary, we have:

Any three points of a line may be projected into any three points of the same line by (not more than) three perspectivities.

Any harmonic set of points may be projected into any other harmonic set.

For, if A, B, C of the harmonic set $H(AC, BD)$ are projected into A', B', C' of the other set $H(A'C', B'D')$, the point D must be projected into D' (p. 39).

We have already called attention to the fact that two distinct points A and C divide a (projective) line into two segments (p. 15). If B is a point of one of these seg-

| A | B | C | D | | B | A | | C | D |

B, D *separate* A, C B, D *do not separate* A, C

FIG. 20

ments and D is a point of the other, the points B and D are said to *separate* the points A and C. In this case, a continuous motion on the line from B to D must pass over one or the other of the points A or C. If, on the other hand, B and D are on the same segment AC, the points B and D are said *not to separate* A and C;

and a continuous motion on the line from B to D is always possible which does not pass over either A or C. (Fig. 20).

The conjugate pairs of a harmonic set always separate each other.

By constructing a harmonic set $H(AC, BD)$ we may observe that the pair A, C does as a matter of fact separate the pair B, D. We have proved that any other harmonic set is projective with the one constructed (p. 45). Furthermore, any projective transformation is a continuous transformation, since each of the perspectivities of which it is the resultant is continuous (p. 16). Hence the pairs of any other harmonic set must separate each other.

In preparation for the proof of the fundamental theorem we need to become familiar with the concept of a point *harmonically related* to three given points. A point X of line u is said to be *harmonically related* to three distinct points A, B, C of u, if X is one of a sequence of points $A, B, C, P_1, P_2, P_3, \cdots, P_{n-1}, P_n = X$, such that P_1 is the harmonic conjugate of one the points A, B, C with respect to the other two, and such that any subsequent point P_i is the harmonic conjugate of one of the preceding points of the sequence with respect to two other preceding points of the sequence. The set of all points on a line harmonically related to three given distinct points A, B, C of the line is called the *net of rationality determined by* A, B, C. The concept thus defined of a net of rationality derives its importance, for our present purpose, from the fact that the points of any such net are "everywhere dense" on the line; i.e., on any segment determined by two distinct points M, N of such a net there exist points of the net. This follows at once from the fact that the contrary assumption, viz. that on one of the segments MN are no points of the net, would imply that all the points of the net are on the other segment. But the harmonic conjugate with respect to M, N of any of these points would then be on the former segment (p. 46), which obviously contradicts the assumption.

(A net of rationality on a line may be shown to be equivalent to the set of points on the line whose coordinates are rational numbers. This accounts for the name, and may also be helpful to the reader in grasping the essential character of such a net.)

We may now prove a lemma from which the Fundamental Theorem will follow readily:

A projective transformation between the points of a given line, which leaves three distinct points of the line fixed, leaves every point of the line fixed.

For, a projective transformation which leaves the three distinct points A, B, C fixed obviously leaves every point of the net of rationality determined by A, B, C fixed. A projective transformation which leaves A, B, C fixed, therefore leaves fixed every point of a set of points which is everywhere dense on the line. Such a transformation, being continuous, therefore leaves every point on the line fixed.

THE FUNDAMENTAL THEOREM OF PROJECTIVE GE-OMETRY. *A projectivity between two one-dimensional primitive forms is completely determined if the correspondents of three distinct elements of one of the forms are given.*

More precisely, and stated for two pencils of points, the theorem may be stated as follows:

If by one sequence of perspectivities we have ABCD
$\overline{\wedge} A'B'C'D'$ *(A, B, C being distinct points) and by another*
sequence of perspectivities we have $ABCD \overline{\wedge} A'B'C'D_1'$,
then will $D' = D_1'$.

In order to prove this we may note that the second
sequence of perspectivities, taken in the reverse order,
followed by the first sequence of perspectivities obviously gives a projectivity which leaves A', B', C'
fixed and transforms D_1 into D_1', in symbols

$$A'B'C'D_1' \overline{\wedge} A'B'C'D'.$$

By the preceding lemma, however, this last projectivity
must leave D_1' fixed. Hence $D' = D_1'$. As an important
corollary, we have the following:

If in a projectivity between the points of two distinct
lines the point of intersection of the two lines corresponds
to itself, the projectivity is a perspectivity.

For, if the point of intersection of the two lines is
$A = A'$, and if the projectivity is determined by ABC
$\overline{\wedge} A'B'C'$, the perspectivity whose center is the intersection of BB' and CC' satisfies the condition defining
the projectivity.

As to the significance of the fundamental theorem, we
may observe that in defining a projectivity we allow
any number of perspectivities to be involved. We have
seen, however, that two perspectivities are sufficient
to project any three distinct points of one line into
any three distinct points of any other line, and the
fundamental theorem tells us that by means of such
three pairs of corresponding points any projectivity
is completely determined. The result of a sequence of
any number of perspectivities may, therefore, be ob-

tained as a result of a sequence of only two such perspectivities, if the correspondence is between the points of two different lines; or as the result of at most three such perspectivities, if the correspondence is between the points of the same line. Any projectivity between the points of two distinct lines may be constructed, therefore, by means of the process used on p. 44.

The reader, furthermore, should not neglect to make himself thoroughly familiar with the plane duals of the theorems and constructions of the present chapter. Thus the plane dual of the construction just referred to gives the construction for a projective correspondence between the lines of two pencils of lines, when three pairs of corresponding lines are given. The reader should have no difficulty in working out this dual construction for himself.

15. Axis of homology. A second and often very convenient method of constructing a projectivity between two one-dimensional primitive forms of the same kind results from the following considerations, in which we confine our discussion to the case of two pencils of points on different lines.

Let u and u' be the two lines (in the same plane) and let a projectivity make the points $A, B, C, D, \cdots$ of u correspond respectively to the points $A', B', C', D', \cdots$ of u' (Fig. 21). If we project these points from A' and A, respectively, we obtain the two projective pencils of lines $AA', AB', AC', AD', \cdots$ and $A'A, A'B, A'C, A'D, \cdots$ in which the line AA' is self-corresponding. By the dual of the corollary to the Fundamental Theorem (p. 48) these two pencils of

lines are, therefore, perspective; the pairs of homologous
lines AB' and $A'B$, AC' and $A'C$, AD' and $A'D$, $\cdots$,
therefore, intersect in points of a line v. Moreover, if O
is the point of intersection of the lines u, u' and U' is
the point of u' which corresponds to O considered as a
point of u, and U is the correspondent of O considered
as a point of u', it is clear that the line v passes through
U and U', i.e., is determined by U and U'. The line v

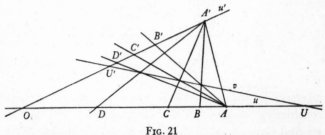

Fig. 21

is then independent of the particular pair of homologous
points, A, A' chosen as centers of the two perspective
pencils. The result of this discussion may be stated as
follows:

*If the points of two distinct lines in the same plane are
projective, $ABCD \cdots \overline{\wedge} A'B'C'D' \cdots$, the pairs of
lines AB' and $A'B$, AC' and $A'C$, BC' and $B'C$, $\cdots$
intersect on a line.*

This line is called the *axis of homology* of the projectivity.

The proof above does not apply if O is a self-
corresponding point. In this case, however, the projectivity between u and u' is a perspectivity (p. 48),
and the pairs of lines mentioned in the theorem are
readily seen to intersect in the points of a line v passing

through O. Indeed, if the center of perspectivity of u and u' is S, the triangles $AB'C$ and $A'BC'$ are perspective from S (Fig. 22). The pairs of homologous sides AB' and $A'B$, BC' and $B'C$, AC' and $A'C$ therefore

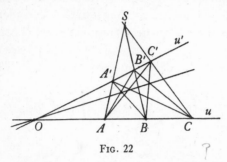

FIG. 22

intersect in collinear points one of which is O. By considering the perspective triangles ABC' and $A'B'C$, we find similarly that the pairs of sides AB and $A'B'$, BC' and $B'C$, AC' and $A'C$ intersect in collinear points one of which is O and one other of which coincides with the intersection of one of the previous pairs. This proves the theorem also for the case in which the projectivity is a perspectivity, in which case the axis of homology passes through the point of intersection of the lines u and u'.

The plane dual of the last theorem is as follows:

If two pencils of lines on distinct centers, but in the same plane, are projective, $abcd \cdots \overline{\wedge} a'b'c'd' \cdots$, the lines joining the pairs of points ab' and $a'b$, ac' and $a'c$, bc' and $b'c$, $\cdots$ are concurrent.

The point in which these lines are concurrent is called the *center of homology* of the projectivity. If the pencils of lines are not perspective, the center of homology is the point of intersection of the two lines which correspond to the common line of the two pencils considered first as a line of one pencil and then as a line of the other pencil.

The reader will note that three pairs of homologous elements determine the axis (center) of homology, and that by means of the latter any number of other pairs of homologous elements are readily constructed.

16. Double elements. Elliptic, parabolic, and hyperbolic projectivities. We consider now certain properties of projectivities among the elements of one and the same primitive form. If in a projectivity on a line a point M corresponds to itself, M is called a *double-point* of the projectivity; similarly, if in a projectivity in a pencil of lines a line m corresponds to itself, m is called a *double-line* of the projectivity.

By the Fundamental Theorem, a projectivity which does not leave every element fixed cannot leave more than two distinct elements fixed. Three possibilities then present themselves:

A projectivity may not have any double elements, in which case it is called *elliptic*.

A projectivity may have a single double element in which case it is called *parabolic*.

A projectivity may have two distinct double elements, in which case it is called *hyperbolic*.

We will now prove the following theorem:

If a projectivity on a line has one double point, it has in general a second, which may, however, coincide with the first.

To prove it, let M be a double point and let A, A' and B, B' be two pairs of homologous points on the line

u (Fig. 23). Take two points S, S' collinear with M
and project the points M, A, B and M, A', B' from S
and S' respectively. The projectivity $S(MAB \cdots)$
$\overline{\wedge} S'(MA'B' \cdots)$ has the self-corresponding line
$SM = S'M$ and is therefore perspective (p. 48). The

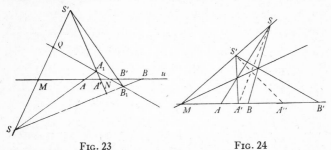

Fɪɢ. 23   Fɪɢ. 24

pairs of lines SA and $S'A'$, SB and $S'B'$, $\cdots$ intersect
in the axis of perspectivity A_1B_1. The point N in
which A_1B_1 meets u is clearly a double point of the
projectivity on u. The point N will in general be distinct from M, but may coincide with M (if A_1B_1 passes
through M). This proves the theorem.

A projectivity with double point M will be parabolic,
i.e., having M as its only double point, if and only if
with the notation of the last paragraph the line A_1B_1
passes through M. This shows how to construct a
parabolic projectivity having given the double point
and one pair of distinct homologous points A, A'.
See Fig. 24.

The preceding considerations prove the existence of
hyperbolic and parabolic projectivities in one-dimensional primitive forms; they also show how to construct
a hyperbolic or a parabolic projectivity if the double
points (the double point) and another pair of homolo-

gous points are given; finally, they show how to construct a second double point if one double point and two pairs of homologous points are given. The actual existence of elliptic projectivities will appear presently.

Before leaving the subject of parabolic projectivities we may use Fig. 24 to prove another theorem concerning them. If A'' is the point into which A' is transformed by the parabolic projectivity which has M for double point and which transforms A into A', the figure shows that A'' is the harmonic conjugate of A with respect to M and A'. Hence, we have the theorem:

If a parabolic projectivity with double point M transforms A into A' and A' into A'', the pairs M, A' and A, A'' separate each other harmonically.

The following theorem on hyperbolic projectivities is important.

If in a hyperbolic projectivity with double points M, N we have $MNAB \barwedge MNA'B'$, *we have also* $MNAA' \barwedge MNBB'$.

In fact, if we refer to Fig. 23 and denote by Q the intersection of the lines SS' and A_1B_1, we have at once

$$ MNAA' \overset{A_1}{\barwedge} MQSS' \overset{B_1}{\barwedge} MNBB'. $$

17. **Involutions.** If a projectivity on a line transforms a point A into a distinct point A', and transforms A' into A, the points A, A' are said to *correspond to each other doubly.*

If, in a projectivity on a line, any two distinct points correspond to each other doubly, every two homologous points correspond to each other doubly.

To prove this, let A, A' be two distinct points that correspond to each other doubly, and let B, B' be any other pair of homologous points (Fig. 25). Let u_1 be

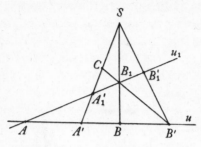

FIG. 25

any line through A distinct from the line AA' and project A', B, B' from a center S into A_1', B_1, B_1' on u_1. Then, if the line $B'B_1$ meets $A'S$ in C, we have

$$AA'BB' \overset{S}{\wedge} AA_1'B_1B_1' \overset{B'}{\wedge} A'A_1'CS \overset{B_1}{\wedge} A'AB'B$$

so that

$$AA'BB' \overline{\wedge} A'AB'B.$$

This shows that the projectivity which is determined by the three homologous pairs $AA'B \overline{\wedge} A'AB'$ must transform B' into B. As a corollary, we have at once the theorem:

If A, A', B, B' are any four points of a line, there exists a projectivity which makes $AA'BB' \overline{\wedge} A'AB'B$.

A projectivity in which every two homologous elements correspond to each other doubly is called an *involution*. It brings about a mere pairing of the elements of the form, and any such pair of homologous elements is called a *conjugate pair* of the involution. *Two such conjugate pairs determine an involution completely* (p. 48). If three pairs of points are conjugate pairs of the same involution, the three pairs are said to be *in involution*.

If an involution has double points M, N and if A, A' are any pair of the involution, then A and A' are harmonic conjugates with respect to M and N.

This follows at once from the construction for the projectivity $MAA' \barwedge MA'A$. (p. 53.) Consequently, if an involution has one double point, it must have a second distinct from the first. An involution is therefore either hyperbolic of elliptic.

It is readily seen that two conjugate pairs of a hyperbolic involution never separate each other. For, if M, N are the distinct double points of such an involution and A, A' are any conjugate pair of the involution, the latter transforms the segment AMA' into the segment $A'MA$ which is the same segment in the opposite sense. The point conjugate to any point B of this segment is therefore also a point of this segment. Similarly for the segment ANA'. Two conjugate pairs of this involution cannot then separate each other. It follows that an involution in which two pairs of conjugate points separate each other is elliptic, which proves the existence of elliptic projectivities.

Moreover, if the pairs A, A' and B, B' do not separate each other, as a point P describes the segment ABA', its conjugate P' describes the same segment $A'B'A$ in the opposite direction. There must then be a point on this segment where P and P' coincide. Hence we have the theorem:

An involution is elliptic or hyperbolic according as two conjugate pairs do or do not separate each other.

A theorem of fundamental importance is the following:

A line (not containing a vertex) cuts the pairs of opposite sides of a complete quadrangle in three pairs of an involution.

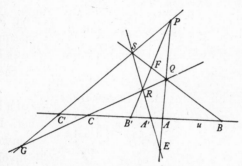

FIG. 26

The proof follows readily from Fig. 26. Let the pairs of opposite sides of the complete quadrangle $PQRS$ cut the line u in the pairs of points A, A'; B, B'; C, C' as indicated. Since the diagonal points of a complete quadrangle are not collinear (p. 36), at least one of these pairs of points must consist of distinct points. Let A, A' be such a pair, and let E be the diagonal point determined by the pair of opposite sides PQ and SR of the quadrangle which determine A and A'. We then have

$$AA'B'C' \overset{P}{\wedge} EA'RS \overset{Q}{\wedge} AA'CB ;$$

also, by a previous theorem (p. 55) $AA'CB \wedge A'ABC$

Hence,

$$AA'B'C' \overline{\wedge} A'ABC.$$

This shows that in the involution defined by $AA'B'$ $\overline{\wedge} A'AB$ the points C, C' are conjugate, or in other words, that the three pairs A, A'; B, B'; C, C' are in involution.

The last theorem furnishes us with a construction for finding the conjugate C' of a point C in the involution determined by the pairs A, A' and B, B'. All that is needed to this end, is to construct a complete quadrangle of which two pairs of opposite sides pass through the two pairs of points A, A' and B, B' and of which one of the remaining sides passes through C; the sixth side of the quadrangle will then pass through C'.

As a corollary of the next to the last theorem we have: *If two pairs of points on a line do not separate each other, there exists one and only one pair of points on the line which separates each of the given pairs harmonically; but if the two given pairs separate each other there exists no pair which separates each of them harmonically.*

For, a pair of points which separates each of two given pairs harmonically must be double points of the involution defined by the given pairs (p. 56). The latter involution has double points if and only if the given pairs do not separate each other (p. 57).

If we think of the two given pairs as the double points of two hyperbolic involutions, a pair that separates each pair of double points harmonically is a common conjugate pair of the two involutions. This shows that *two hyperbolic involutions on the same line have a conjugate pair in common if and only if the double points of the involutions do not separate each other.*

This raises a question that is important in some later developments as to the conditions under which two involutions on the same line have a conjugate pair in common. The question has been answered in the preceding paragraph for the case in which both the involutions are hyperbolic. There remain the cases in which one or both of the involutions are elliptic. Let I and I_1 denote the two involutions in question and suppose that I transforms a point A into A', while I_1 transforms A' into A_1'. Let I_1I denote the projectivity which is the resultant of these two involutions taken in this order; i.e., the projectivity which transforms A into A_1'. It is clear that if M, N constitute a conjugate pair both of I and of I_1 both M and N are double points of the projectivity I_1I; and conversely. Our question as to whether I and I_1 have or have not a common conjugate pair reduces to the question whether the projectivity I_1I has or has not double points.

To answer this question it is desirable to introduce the distinction between *direct* and *opposite* projectivities. Given any projectivity on a line, let it transform the point P into P'. Suppose P moves continuously on the line in one of the two possible directions; P' will then also move continuously on the line (p. 46), and if the motion of P' is in the same direction as that of P the projectivity is said to be *direct*; if P' moves in the direction opposite to that of P the projectivity is said to be *opposite*. An opposite projectivity always has double points, for if the points P and P' move in opposite directions on the line there must be points on the line at which P and P' coincide. We have, indeed, already made use of this argument when we discussed

the existence of double points of an involution (p. 56)
We found that a hyperbolic involution is always opposite, whereas an elliptic involution is always direct.
In the case of projectivities that are not involutions
the situation is not so simple, in view of the fact that
a direct non-involutoric projectivity may have a double
point.

To return to our problem, if one of the involutions
I, I_1 is elliptic and the other is hyperbolic, we know that
one is direct and the other opposite. The projectivity
I_1I is, therefore, opposite and must have double points.
An elliptic and a hyperbolic involution then always
have a common conjugate pair. If, finally, both of the
involutions I, I_1 are elliptic the projectivity I_1I is
direct and further investigation is necessary. Let A' be
the conjugate of A with respect to I, and let A_1, A_1' be
the conjugates respectively of A, A' under I_1. The projectivity I_1I transforms A into A_1' and A' into A_1, and
is direct. Moreover, since I_1 is elliptic, the pairs A, A_1
and A', A_1' separate each other (p. 57). Hence, it is
easy to see that one of the directions on the line will
make the four points in question come in the order
A, A', A_1, A_1'. As a point P
describes the segment AA'
in the direction indicated,
its corresponding point P'
under the projectivity I_1I will describe the segment
$A_1'A_1$ in the same direction. The segment AA' is contained in the segment $A_1'A_1$ and hence there must be
on the segment AA' a point M where P and P' coincide; i.e., the projectivity I_1I must have a double point.
It must have another double point $N(\neq M)$, since the

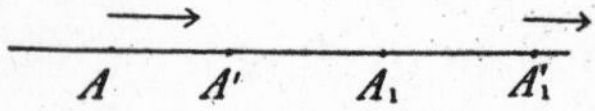

FIG. 27

conjugate of M under I must be identical with the conjugate of M under I_1. The two points M and N constitute a common conjugate pair of I and I_1. Hence, we have the theorem: *Two involutions one of which at least is elliptic always have a common conjugate pair.*

In the preceding argument we assumed tacitly that A' and A_1 are distinct. If, however, we had $A' = A_1$ the pair A, A' would be a common pair of the two involutions, and no further argument would be necessary.

CHAPTER V

THE PASCAL AND BRIANCHON THEOREMS

18. Definition of point conic and line conic. If S and S' ($S \neq S'$) are the centers of two pencils of lines in the same plane, and a projective correspondence is established between the lines of the two pencils, to every line of the pencil S will correspond a uniquely determined line of the pencil S'. The points of intersection of all such pairs of corresponding lines will constitute a curve which is called a *point conic*. If the projectivity between the two generating pencils of lines is perspective, the points of intersection will all lie on a straight line, the axis of perspectivity, and on the line SS' which is self-corresponding. This case of a so-called "degenerate" point conic is to be excluded, at least for the present. We are thus led to the following definition: The locus of the points of intersection of pairs of corresponding lines of two projective, non-perspective, pencils of lines on distinct centers in the same plane is called a *point conic*.

A projective correspondence between two pencils of lines is, by the fundamental theorem (p. 47), completely determined when three pairs of corresponding lines are given. If the lines a, b, c of the pencil S correspond respectively to the lines a', b', c' of S', the points $aa' = A$, $bb' = B$, and $cc' = C$ are, by definition, points of the point conic; conversely, if S and S' are given as the centers of two generating pencils, and three other

non-collinear points A, B, C are given, a point conic
generated by pencils at S and S' and passing through
the points A, B, C is uniquely determined.

We may note at once
that the point conic
thus determined passes
through S and S'. For,
to the line SS' con-
sidered as a line of the
pencil S corresponds a
line t' of S', and this
pair of corresponding
lines intersect at S';

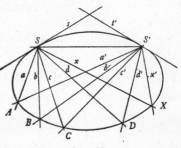

Fig. 28

similarly, the line $S'S$ considered as a line of the pencil
S', is the correspondent of a line s of S, and this pair
of corresponding lines intersect at S. Furthermore, the
line t' obviously has no other point in common with
the point conic than S', and the line s meets the conic
in the point S only. If then we define a *tangent* to the
point conic as being a line in the plane of the point
conic and meeting the point conic in only one point,
we see that the lines s and t' are both tangents. It is,
moreover, clear also that s and t' are limiting positions
of the lines x and x' respectively, as X approaches S
or S' along the point conic. The lines s and t' are then
tangents also according to the latter definition.

The plane dual of the definition of a point conic is
as follows: The set of all lines joining the pairs of corresponding points of two projective, non-perspective,
pencils of points on distinct lines in the same plane is
called a *line conic*. A point in the plane of a line conic
through which passes only one line of the line conic is

called a *point of contact* of the line conic. This is the plane dual of the idea of a tangent to a point conic.

19. The construction of a point conic from the definition. We will now see how to construct a point conic generated by two pencils at two given points S and S' and containing three given non-collinear points A, B, C (Fig. 29). The projectivity between the generating pencils is determined by the three pairs of corresponding lines a, a'; b, b'; c, c' where $a = SA$, $a' = S'A$; $b = SB$, $b' = S'B$; $c = SC$, $c' = S'C$.

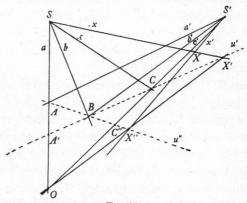

FIG. 29

Given any other line x through S, we must learn how to determine its corresponding line x' through S'. To this end, draw the lines $BC = u'$ and $AB = u''$, and let a, b, c, x meet u' in A', B, C, X', and let a', b', c' meet u'' in A, B, C'', respectively. The projectivity between the lines of the pencils S and S' gives rise to the projectivity

$$A'BCX' \overline{\wedge} ABC''X''$$

between the points of u' and u'', where X'' is a point still to be determined. But this latter projectivity is

perspective, since the point B corresponds to itself
(p. 48). The center of this perspectivity is obviously
the intersection O of the lines AA' and CC''. To determine the unknown point X'', therefore, we need only
find the intersection of u'' with OX'. The line x' of the
pencil S' is then the line $S'X''$, and the point of intersection X of x and x' is another point of the point conic.
In this way any number of points of the point conic may
be constructed. However, this method of construction
becomes much clearer by a restatement which involves
a very remarkable theorem, known as Pascal's Theorem.
We will accordingly turn our attention to the latter,
and postpone for the present the problem of constructing a conic.

20. **Pascal's theorem.** In order to put the result of
the last paragraph into a more usable form and thereby
to gain a proof of Pascal's Theorem, we must introduce
the idea of a *simple plane hexagon*. The figure formed
by six coplanar points, $ABCDEF$, no three of which are
collinear, *taken in a given cyclical order*, together with
the six lines joining pairs of *successive* points, is called
a *simple plane hexagon*. The six points are called the
vertices of the hexagon, and the six lines are called the
sides. Moreover, these sides go in pairs of so-called
opposite sides, the sides AB and DE being opposite,
likewise BC and EF, and CD and FA. Also, the vertices A and D, B and E, C and F are said to be *opposite*.

We now return to the result of the last paragraph.
Let us consider the simple hexagon $SABCS'X$ determined by the six points of our point conic in the order
indicated. The pairs of opposite sides of this hexagon
intersect as follows:

SA and CS' intersect in O ;

AB and $S'X$ intersect in X'' ;

BC and XS intersect in X'.

But, the points O, X'', X' are by construction collinear. This result may be stated as follows:

If A, B, C, X are any four points of a point conic generated by pencils of lines at S and S', the pairs of opposite sides of the simple hexagon $SABCS'X$ will meet in three collinear points.

The converse of this theorem can be readily verified. The simple hexagon $CS'XSAB$ is, however, the same hexagon as $SABCS'X$. Hence, if A, B, C, X are points of a point conic generated by pencils at S and S', then also will S', X, S, B, be points of a point conic generated by pencils at C and A. Three points in addition to the centers of the generating pencils determine a point conic completely. The two point conics are then determined by the centers S, S' and the three points A, B, C, and by the centers C, A and the three points S', S, B, respectively. The result obtained states that if X is any point of the first point conic, it is a point of the second point conic also; in other words, the two point conics coincide. This proves the following fundamental theorem:

A point conic is uniquely determined by any five of its points; and may be generated by projective pencils whose centers are any two of its points.

This theorem, however, shows that the six points S, S', A, B, C, X are any points of the point conic. This gives at once the following theorem:

PASCAL'S THEOREM. *A necessary and sufficient condition that six points be points of a point conic is that the pairs of opposite sides of any simple hexagon having these points as vertices meet in collinear points.*

This theorem was proved by Blaise Pascal (1623–1662) when only sixteen years of age, a remarkable example of mathematical precocity. His method was of course different from the one here given. He proved the theorem first for the circle and thence inferred its validity for any point conic, from the fact that any such conic could be obtained from a circle by the method of projection and section. The reader must, at present, take on faith the fact that "point-conic" as we have defined it is the ordinary conic with which he has become familiar in earlier studies. (See the end of Chapter VI.)

In view of its importance we will state the theorem also as follows:

If 1, 2, 3, 4, 5, 6, *are points of a point conic, the points of intersection of the pairs of lines* 12 *and* 45, 23 *and* 56, 34 *and* 61 *are on a straight line; and conversely.*

This line is called the *Pascal line* of the hexagon 123456.

From a set of six given points 60 different simple hexagons may be formed. Each of these hexagons gives rise to a Pascal line. The sixty lines thus obtained from six points of a point conic form a very remarkable configuration which was not unnaturally given the name of *Hexagrammum Mysticum*. Its study is, however, beyond the scope of the present monograph. (See Veblen and Young, *Projective Geometry*, vol. I, p. 138, Ex. 19.)

21. The construction of the point conic through five given points. Pascal's Theorem furnishes a simple method for constructing a point conic through five given points; i.e., for constructing as many points of the point conic as you please.   To this end let 1, 2, 3, 4, 5 be the given points of a point conic.   We will show how to construct the sixth point 6 on any line through

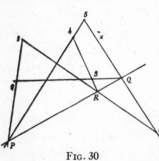

Fig. 30

5. Let x be any such line through the point 5. The intersection P of the lines 12 and 45 is a point of the Pascal line of the hexagon 123456; the intersection Q of the lines 23 and $x(=56)$ is a second point of this Pascal line. This line is then determined. According to Pascal's Theorem, therefore, the line PQ must meet 34 in a point R through which 61 must also pass. This determines the line 61, and the intersection of 61 and x $(=56)$ gives the desired point 6. The construction can be readily repeated for other lines x through 5.

22. Brianchon's Theorem. The plane dual of Pascal's theorem is as follows:

BRIANCHON'S THEOREM. *A necessary and sufficient condition that six lines be lines of a line conic is that the lines joining the pairs of opposite vertices of any simple hexagon having the given lines as sides are concurrent.*

This theorem may also be stated as follows:

If 1, 2, 3, 4, 5, 6 are lines of a line conic the lines joining the pairs of vertices 12 and 45, 23 and 56, 34 and 61 are concurrent.

This theorem may evidently be used in a manner analogous to the use of Pascal's Theorem, to construct a line conic when any five of its lines are given. Fig. 31 exhibits this construction. The lines 1, 2, 3, 4, 5 are the given lines; a sixth line 6 of the conic is to be constructed through an arbitrary point X on the line

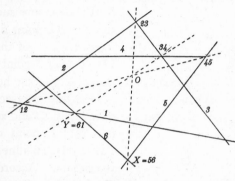

FIG. 31

5. The lines joining the points 12 and 45, and 23 and $X = 56$, determine the Brianchon point O. The desired line 6 must then meet line 1 in the point $Y = 61$ in which the line joining 34 and O meets 1. XY is then the desired line. Brianchon's Theorem was not noted until the early years of the nineteenth century.

23. Tangents. Points of contact. A line in the plane of a point conic which meets the conic in one and only one point P is called a *tangent* to the point conic *at the point P*. A point in the plane of a line conic through which passes one and only one line p of the line conic is called a *point of contact* of the line conic *on the line p*.

Through any point of a point conic there is one and only one tangent to the point conic.

For, let A be the given point of the conic, let B be any other point, and let P be a variable point of the conic. We then have the pencil of lines at A projective with the pencil at B, if pairs of homologous lines pass through P (p. 66). Any line through A meets its homologous line through B in a point distinct from A, except when its homologous line is BA. Since a projective correspondence is one-to-one, there is only one line through A whose homologous line is BA. The plane dual of this theorem is as follows:

On any line of a line conic there is one and only one point of contact of the line conic.

24. Special cases of Pascal's Theorem. A tangent to a point conic may also be considered as the limiting position of a secant as the points of intersection of the secant with the conic approach coincidence. By considering the various limiting cases that arise when we think of two of the vertices of a simple hexagon inscribed in a point conic as approaching coincidence, we obtain a number of important special cases of Pascal's Theorem and, by duality, of Brianchon's Theorem.

Suppose first that the vertices 1 and 2 coincide. The side 12 is then a tangent to the conic at the point $1 = 2$. Pascal's Theorem then states that the tangent 12 and the side 45 meet in a point which is on the line joining the points of intersection of 23 and 56 and of 34 and 61. In other words:

If the vertices of a simple pentagon are points of a point conic, the tangent to the conic at one of the vertices meets the opposite side in a point collinear with the points of intersection of the other two pairs of opposite sides. (See Fig. 32).

By a similar argument, if we think of the side 12 as being a tangent (1 = 2) and the side 34 as also being a tangent (3 = 4), we obtain the following:

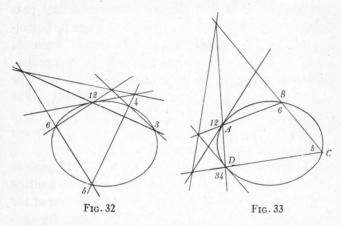

Fig. 32   Fig. 33

If the vertices A, B, C, D of a simple quadrangle are points of a point conic, the tangent at A and the side CD, the tangent at D and the side AB, and the pair of sides AD and BC meet in three collinear points. (Fig. 33)

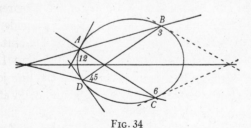

Fig. 34

If, on the other hand we think of two opposite sides, 12 and 45, of our hexagon as being tangents (1 = 2 and 4 = 5), the theorem becomes:

*If the vertices of a complete quadrangle are points of a
point conic, the tangents at two of the vertices meet in a
point of the line joining the diagonal points of the quadrangle which are not on the side joining the two vertices.*
(Fig. 34)

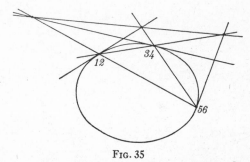

Fig. 35

Finally, if we think of three of the sides of our hexagon
as being tangents, we obtain:

*If three points are points of a point conic, the tangent at
each point and the line joining the other two points meet
in collinear points; or, a triangle inscribed in a point conic
and the triangle formed by the tangents at its vertices are
perspective.* (Fig. 35)

25. **The tangents to a point conic form a line conic.**
A further consideration of one of the theorems (p. 71)
of the last section will yield an important result. Let
A, B, C, P be four points of a point conic (Fig. 36), and
let a, b, c, p be the tangents at these points, respectively.
By the theorem just referred to, the intersection of the
tangents b and c is on the line joining the diagonal points
R and Q of the quadrangle $ABCP$. By the same theorem,
the intersection of the tangents a and p is also on the
line RQ. By similar reasoning we see that the points ac,

bp, and Q are collinear. Now, the line AB is the axis of homology (p. 50) of the projectivity between the pencils of points on a and b defined by

$$A(ab)(ac) \; \overline{\wedge} \; (ba)B(bc).$$

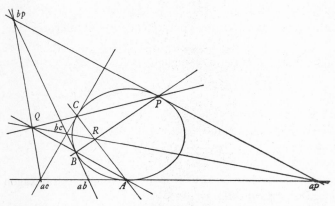

Fig. 36

Hence, the point corresponding in this projectivity to ap is the point bp; i.e., if p is thought of as a variable tangent, it is the line joining pairs of homologous points on the two lines a and b, so that the totality of lines p satisfies the definition of a line conic. We have, therefore, the following theorems:

The tangents to a point conic form a line conic;

and the plane dual of this theorem:

The points of contact of a line conic form a point conic.

We may now define a self-dual figure called a *conic* as a point conic together with its tangents (or, as a line conic together with its points of contact). In forming plane duals of theorems regarding conics it is clear that the word *conic* is left unchanged while the words *point*

(of a conic) and *line* or *tangent* (of a conic) are interchanged. If the points of a plane figure are on a conic,
the figure is said to be *inscribed* in the conic; if the lines
of a plane figure are tangent to a conic, the figure is
said to be *circumscribed* about the conic. The duals of
Pascal's Theorem and its special cases now give us
theorems of the same consequence for point conics as
for line conics. By way of illustration we will restate
Brianchon's Theorem from this point of view:

BRIANCHON'S THEOREM: *If a simple hexagon is circumscribed about a conic, the lines joining opposite vertices are concurrent; and conversely.*

Another important theorem follows readily from the
last figure:

*If A is a fixed and P is a variable point of a conic, and
a and p are the tangents at these two points respectively,
then we have* $A\,[P] \overline{\wedge} a\,[p]$.

The proof follows readily from the notation in Fig.
36: We have, first,

$$A\,[P] \overline{\wedge} C\,[P] \overline{\wedge} [Q],$$

where $[Q]$ is the pencil of points on AB. We also have

$$[Q] \frac{ac}{\wedge} b\,[p],$$

and (by p. 66, dual),

$$b\,[p] \overline{\wedge} a\,[p].$$

Combining these projectivities, we have

$$A\,[P] \overline{\wedge} a\,[p].$$

26. **Pole and polar with respect to a conic.** Let us
consider a conic and a point P in the plane of the conic

but not on the conic. Let AB and CD be any two lines
through P and cutting the conic in A, B and C, D,
respectively, and let the intersection of AD and BC
be denoted by Q, that of AC and BD by R (Fig. 37).
It is then clear (from p. 71) that the intersections
H, K of the tangents to the conic at A and B and at C
and D, respectively, are on the line QR. Furthermore,
if QR meets the line AB in M, it is evident from the

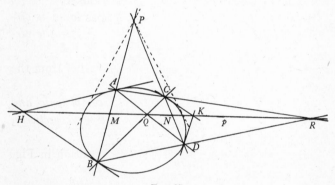

Fig. 37

figure that M is the harmonic conjugate of P with
respect to A and B, since the latter points are diagonal
points of the complete quadrangle $RCQD$ and the
opposite sides CD and RQ pass through P and M
respectively. For a similar reason, the point N in which
the line QR meets the line CD is the harmonic conjugate of P with respect to C and D. The line $p = QR$
then contains the points H, K, M, and N; it is therefore
determined by the points H and M and these points
depend only on the line AB through P. If then we
think of the line ABP as fixed and think of the line
CDP as variable we obtain the following theorem:

If P is a point in the plane of a conic, but not on the conic, there exists a uniquely determined line p which contains:

1) *the other two diagonal points of any complete quadrangle inscribed in the conic one of whose diagonal points is P;*

2) *the harmonic conjugate of P with respect to any two points of the conic collinear with P;*

3) *the point of intersection of the tangents to the conic at any two points collinear with P.*

The line p thus uniquely defined by the point P and the conic is called the *polar of P with respect to the conic.* If P is any point of the conic the *polar of P with respect to the conic* is defined to be the tangent to the conic at P.

The plane dual of the last theorem is as follows:

If p is a line in the plane of a conic, but not a tangent to the conic, there exists a uniquely determined point P through which pass:

1) *the other two diagonal lines of any complete quadrilateral circumscribed about the conic one of whose diagonal lines is p;*

2) *the harmonic conjugate of p with respect to any two tangents to the conic which are concurrent with p;*

3) *the line joining the points of contact of any two tangents to the conic which are concurrent with p.*

The point P thus uniquely determined by the line p and the conic is called the *pole of p with respect to the conic.* If the line p is tangent to the conic, the *pole of p with respect to the conic* is defined to be the point of contact of p.

There is thus associated with *every* point in the plane of a conic a unique line, the *polar* of the point; and with *every* line in the plane of a conic a unique point, the *pole* of the line. We proceed to study the relations of poles and polars.

We may note first that the relation of pole and polar is a reciprocal one, as expressed in the following theorem:

If p is the polar of a point P, the point P is the pole of p.

If P is not on the conic, this follows at once by comparing the first 3 with the second 3 on p. 76. If P is on the conic, it follows from the definition. The following is also evident, if a tangent is regarded as the limiting position of a secant:

The polar of a point P with respect to a conic passes through the points of contact of the tangents to the conic through P, if such tangents exist.

27. The polar system of a conic. We have seen how a conic defines a reciprocally one-to-one correspondence between the points and lines of a plane, whereby to every point corresponds its polar and to every line its pole. Such a correspondence is called a *polar system*. We proceed to study its properties a little more fully.

We ask ourselves first: If a point moves along a line p, how does its polar move? We will suppose first that the line p is not tangent to the conic. Let P be the pole of p (which is, then, not on the conic), let Q be any point of p and let A be any point of the conic. Let the lines AP and AQ meet the conic again in B and C respectively, and let PC meet the conic again in D (Fig. 38). One diagonal point of the complete quadrangle $ABCD$ is at P; hence (p. 71) the other two diagonal points are on p. This means that the line BD passes through Q and the lines AD and BC meet in a point

R of p. Hence, the line $q = PR$ is the polar of Q. Now, if we consider the point A and the line p as fixed, the points P and B are also fixed. If we let Q move on p,

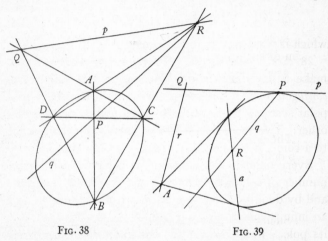

FIG. 38   FIG. 39

the points C and D and the line q will move, the latter, however, always passing through the fixed point P. The pencils of lines $A[C]$ and $B[C]$ are projective (p. 66). Hence, we have

$$[Q] \underset{\wedge}{\overline{}} A[C] \underset{\wedge}{\overline{}} B[C] \underset{\wedge}{\overset{p}{}} [q].$$

The result of this discussion may be stated as follows:

As a point Q moves on a line p, the polar q of Q rotates about the pole P of p, and the pencil of points $[Q]$ is projective with the pencil of lines $[q]$; and conversely.

The proof we have given of this important theorem applies only when p is not tangent to the conic. To prove it when p is tangent to the conic, let P be the point of contact (the pole) of p (Fig. 39). Let Q be any point of p and let A be the intersection of any two fixed tangents of the conic. Denote the line AQ by r, and its pole by R, the latter being on the polar a of A. The line $RP = q$ is evidently the polar of Q. We now have

$$[Q] \mathbin{\overline{\wedge}} [r] \mathbin{\overline{\wedge}} [R] \mathbin{\overline{\wedge}} [q], \text{ or } [Q] \mathbin{\overline{\wedge}} [q],$$

which is what we desired to prove.

28. Conjugate points.   Conjugate lines. We now make a few definitions. Two points are said to be *conjugate* with respect to a conic (or with respect to a polar system), if the polar of either passes through the other. Two lines are said to be *conjugate* with respect to a conic, if the pole of either is on the other.

Every point in the plane of the conic has an infinite number of conjugates, namely the points on its polar; and by duality, every line in the plane of the conic has an infinite number of conjugate lines, the lines through its pole. The only points conjugate with themselves are the points of the conic; the only self-conjugate lines are the tangents of the conic.

Consider a line p not tangent to the conic. Any point Q on p has a conjugate Q' on p, viz., the intersection of p with the polar q of Q. The correspondence Q to Q' is clearly projective (p. 78) and is, moreover, an involution since to Q' corresponds the intersection with p of the polar q' of Q' which passes through Q. Hence we have the following theorem:

On every line not tangent to a conic, there exists an infinite number of pairs of conjugate points with respect to the conic; and these pairs of conjugate points are the pairs of an involution.

We shall refer to this involution as *the involution of conjugate points* on the line.

The plane dual of the last theorem is as follows:

In every pencil of lines whose center is not on a conic there exists an infinite number of pairs of conjugate lines with respect to the conic; and these pairs of conjugate lines are the pairs of an involution.

We note, further, that if and only if a line has points in common with the conic, does the involution of conjugate points on the line have double points, viz., the points in which the line meets the conic. Hence, *the involution of conjugate points on a line (not a tangent to the conic) is elliptic or hyperbolic, according as the line does not or does meet the conic.* Similarly, *the involution of conjugate lines through a point (not on the conic) is elliptic or hyperbolic according as tangents to the conic through the point do not or do exist.*

29. The principle of duality in a plane. We are now in a position to indicate one of the methods of establishing the principle of duality in the plane to which we referred on p. 26. Given any figure F in a plane, let us form the figure F' obtained by replacing every line of F by its pole with respect to a conic in the plane and every point of F by its polar with respect to the same conic. To every point of F corresponds a line of F' and to every line of F corresponds a point of F'. Moreover, whenever a line of F passes through a point of F, the corresponding point of F' is on the corresponding line of F'. If two pencils of points (lines) in F are projective, the corresponding pencils of lines (points) in F' are likewise projective (p. 78). It follows that any projective property of F is reproduced as a corresponding projective property of F' in which the roles played by the points and lines of F are interchanged.

CHAPTER VI

METRIC PROPERTIES

30. Projective and metric properties. We have hitherto confined our attention to purely projective properties of figures; i.e., to properties that remain unchanged under any projective transformations. Conceptions associated with such words as parallel, perpendicular, distance, angle, etc. have had no place in our discussion, and could indeed have no place since they refer to properties which do not remain unchanged under all projective transformations.

However, such metric properties do have relations to projective properties and it is these relations we now propose to consider. Two methods of approach are open to us. The first and simpler of the two is to assume our knowledge of elementary metric (euclidean) geometry and investigate directly the relations between certain of these metric properties and the projective properties of figures with which we have become acquainted in the preceding chapters. It will be recalled that we built up our conception of projective space by adding to the elements of euclidean metric space with which we were already familiar certain ideal or improper elements. To be more specific, we added to our metric space an ideal plane, the plane at infinity. The points and lines of this plane were then the ideal or improper points and lines, the points and lines at infinity as we called them. All the other points, lines, and planes of

space were then proper points. Having by the introduction of the improper points and lines and the improper plane extended our conception of space, we com-
pleted the conception of projective space by wiping out
the distinction between proper and improper elements;
the points, lines, and planes of projective space are
classes of identical elements, the elements of each class
differing among themselves only in position.

The first method of approach to the study of metric
properties in a projective setting consists in re-
establishing this distinction between proper and
improper elements, between ordinary points and lines
and the points and lines at infinity. We should then
recognize that parallel lines, for example, meet on the
line at infinity in the plane of the lines; we would observe, that the harmonic conjugate of the mid-point of
the segment AB of a line is the point at infinity on that
line (see below); we would prove that all the pairs of
perpendicular lines in a plane cut the line at infinity
in that plane in pairs of points of one and the same
involution; etc.

The second method of approach, less elementary but
esthetically more satisfying, would have us forget our
early study of elementary metric geometry and would
have us regard projective geometry as the fundamental
form of geometry, out of which other forms are to be
developed without any previous suppositions and thereby seek to justify Cayley's dictum: "Projective geometry
is all geometry." This method of approach is at the
outset quite as simple as the other method just described, although the point of view is radically different.
According to this second method we assume no previous

knowledge of metric properties whatever. We begin by choosing arbitrarily some (any) plane of our projective space to be an "improper" plane and with reference to this improper plane we make certain definitions. All the points and lines of this plane are said to be improper. Two lines in the same plane are *defined* to be parallel, if they intersect in an improper point; two distinct points A and B being given, the harmonic conjugate of the improper point on the line AB with respect to A and B is *defined* to be the mid-point of AB; we establish arbitrarily any (elliptic) involution on the improper line of a given plane and call it the absolute or orthogonal involution in that plane, and then *define* two lines to be perpendicular to each other if they meet the improper line in a conjugate pair of the orthogonal involution; etc. The reader will note that with these definitions certain of the familiar theorems concerning parallel and perpendicular lines follow immediately. For example, two lines parallel to the same line are parallel to each other; two lines in a plane perpendicular to the same line are parallel; a line in the plane of two parallel lines and perpendicular to one of them is perpendicular to the other also.

In spite of this simplicity at the outset, the second method of approach involves some difficulties if all the metric conceptions are to be defined in projective terms. It seems desirable, therefore, to adopt a combination of these two methods. We begin with the second method of approach, and as hitherto we confine ourselves to figures in the same plane. In this plane we arbitrarily recognize an exceptional line, or improper line, which we call *the line at infinity*, with reference to which and to the (improper) points at infinity on it we make certain definitions. In each case, however, where it seems desirable we will call upon our knowledge of elementary metric geometry to prove that the definitions made are indeed in accordance with our knowledge of such metric geometry. At a later stage we will definitely adopt the first method of approach to get us over certain difficulties. In a later chapter we shall return again to the problem of the second method, that is, the problem of developing the whole of metric geometry on a projective basis.

31. Parallel lines. Midpoint. Two lines in the same plane are said to be *parallel*, if they meet in a point at infinity. It follows at once from this definition that *two lines parallel to the same line are parallel to each other*; and that *through a given point there is one and only one line parallel to a given line*.

Another definition of fundamental importance is the following: Given two distinct points A, B, the harmonic conjugate, M, of the point at infinity on AB is called the *midpoint* of AB, and M is said to *bisect* AB.

It must be kept in mind that from the point of view of the second method of approach described in the preceding section none of the familiar properties of the terms defined must be assumed until such time as they are seen to follow from previously established theorems. That the above definition of midpoint does in-

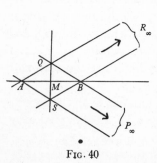

Fig. 40

deed correspond to the concept associated with this term in our elementary metric geometry may be seen as follows (Fig. 40): If two arbitrary lines AQ and AS are drawn through A and lines BS and BQ are drawn through B parallel to AQ and AS respectively, the lines AQ and SB meet, by definition, in a point R at infinity, while AS and QB meet by definition in a point P at infinity. The complete quadrangle $PQRS$ then has two diagonal points at A and B, while the remaining pair of opposite sides pass through M and the point at infinity on the line AB. The point M is then by construction the harmonic conjugate of the point at infinity on AB with respect to A and B. On the other hand, that M is the midpoint of the segment AB follows from the familiar proposition that the diagonals of a parallelogram ($PQRS$) bisect each other.

This is, of course, merely a verification obtained by assuming a knowledge of elementary geometry. From the point of view of the second method of approach described above, the theorem of elementary geometry on which the above verification depends, viz., *the diagonals of a parallelogram bisect each other*, is itself an immediate consequence of the theorems on harmonic sets and the following definitions: A simple quadrangle $ABCD$ in which the sides AB and CD, and also the sides AD and BC, are parallel is called a *parallelogram*; the lines AC and BD are the *diagonals* of the parallelogram.

As another example of how familiar metric theorems appear as special cases of projective theorems we may cite the following:

If the sides AB, BC, CA of a triangle ABC are cut by *a line l (not passing through a vertex) in points C_1, A_1, B_1 respectively, and if C', A', B' are the harmonic conjugates of C_1, A_1, B_1, respectively, with respect to A and B, B and C, C and A, then $B'A'C_1$ are collinear; likewise $A'C'B_1$ are collinear and $B'C'A_1$ are collinear.*

To prove this theorem we need only note that we have (Fig. 41)

$$AB'CB_1 \overset{\wedge}{-} BA'CA_1,$$

since these sets of four points are harmonic sets (p. 45). Since C is self-corresponding this projectivity is a

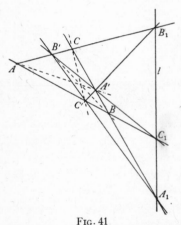

perspectivity (p. 48). Hence, AB, $A'B'$, B_1A_1 are concurrent. But this means that B', A', C_1 are collinear. A similar argument applies to the other sets of three points.

If we specialize this theorem by taking l to be the line at infinity, A', B', C' are by definition the midpoints of the sides BC, CA, AB

Fig. 41

respectively, and the theorem then states that $A'B'$ is parallel to AB, $B'C'$ to BC, and $C'A'$ to CA. In other words, *the line joining the midpoints of two sides of a triangle is parallel to the third side.*

The reader may prove for himself that with the above notation the lines AA', BB', CC' are concurrent. The special case of this result, when l is the line at infinity, gives: *The medians of a triangle meet in a point.*

32. The classification of conics. Confining ourselves to "real" points, as we have hitherto, the line at infinity may meet a conic in two distinct points, may be tangent to it, or may meet it not at all. This gives us the following classification of conics: A conic which meets the line at infinity in two distinct points is called

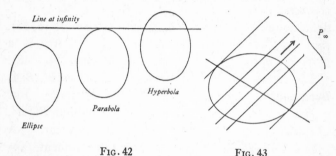

FIG. 42   FIG. 43

a *hyperbola*; a conic tangent to the line at infinity is called a *parabola*; a conic having no point in common with the line at infinity is called an *ellipse*. (See Fig. 42)

We note the following additional definitions: The tangents to a hyperbola at the points where it meets the line at infinity are called *asymptotes*. The pole of the line at infinity with respect to a conic is called the *center* of the conic, and any line through the center is called a *diameter* of the conic. Conics whose centers are proper points are called *central conics* (ellipse and hyperbola).

It should be noted that *every diameter of a conic is the polar with respect to the conic of some point at infinity* (p. 78). We may now state the following theorem:

The midpoints of any system of parallel chords of a conic all lie on a diameter d, conjugate to the diameter which is parallel to the chords; and the diameter d passes through the points of contact, if they exist, of the tangents to the conic which are parallel to the chords. (Fig. 43)

This is an immediate consequence of the definition of midpoint and the theorem defining the polar of a point with respect to a conic (p. 78). Other metric theorems on conics that follow readily from the above definitions and projective theorems on conics previously proved are as follows:

No two (proper) *tangents to a parabola are parallel.*

The asymptotes of a hyperbola meet at the center of the hyperbola.

If a parallelogram is inscribed in a conic, the tangents at a pair of opposite vertices are parallel.

If a parallelogram be circumscribed about a conic, its diagonals meet at the center and are conjugate diameters.

If a parallelogram be inscribed in a conic, two adjacent sides are parallel to conjugate diameters.

The reader will have no difficulty in proving each of these theorems on the basis of the projective theorems with which he is already familiar.

33. Perpendicular lines. The orthogonal involution. As a preliminary to the introduction of the concept of perpendicularity we will assume the proposition from elementary metric geometry that the altitudes of a triangle meet in a point and by means of it prove the following:

All the pairs of perpendicular lines in a plane meet the line at infinity in pairs of points of one and the same involution.

Let ABC be any triangle and let AD, BE, CF be the perpendiculars dropped from the vertices on the opposite sides. By the proposition just referred to these perpendiculars meet in a point M (Fig. 44). The points A, B, C, M are then the vertices of a complete quadrangle the pairs of opposite sides of which meet the line at infinity in pairs of points of an involution I (p. 57). To show that any other pair of perpendicular lines l and l' in the plane meet the line at infinity in a

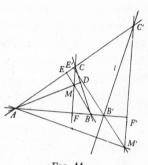

Fig. 44

pair of points of the same involution, let l meet AB and AC in B' and C', respectively. (We may obviously assume that l does not contain A; if it did, choose for l another line parallel to l not containing A.) The perpendiculars $B'E'$ and $C'F'$ drawn from B' and C' to AC and AB respectively are parallel to BE and CF and intersect in a point M'. The involution determined on the line at infinity by the pairs of opposite sides of the quadrangle $AB'C'M'$ has two pairs in common with the involution I determined by the quadrangle $ABCM$ and is hence identical with I (p 56). Therefore, l and the line AM', which is perpendicular to $B'C' = l$, meet the line at infinity in a conjugate pair of I. Any line l' perpendicular to l is parallel to AM' and meets the line at infinity in the same point as AM'. This proves the proposition.

Moreover, *the involution I is evidently elliptic.* since

any line through a double point of I would be perpendicular to itself and no such (real) lines exist.

Adopting now the second method of approach to metric properties we may lay down the following definitions. Let I be an arbitrary but fixed elliptic involution on the line at infinity. This involution I we will call the *orthogonal* or *absolute involution*. Two lines are said to be *perpendicular* if they pass through a conjugate pair of the orthogonal involution.

The following results follow immediately from this definition:

The pairs of perpendicular lines in a pencil of lines are conjugate pairs of an involution.

The involution of perpendicular lines in a pencil of lines is called the *circular involution* of the pencil.

Through any point there is one and only one line perpendicular to a given line.

A line perpendicular to one of two parallel lines is perpendicular to the other.

Two lines perpendicular to the same line are parallel.

34. Angle bisectors. If two perpendicular lines are harmonic with two lines a, b through their point of intersection, the perpendicular lines are said to *bisect* the angles formed by a and b.

That this definition does indeed correspond to the familiar notion of bisectors may be seen as follows: Let the two perpendicular lines be m and n and let a line perpendicular to m and hence parallel to n meet a, b, m, n in the points A, B, M, N, the latter being at infinity (Fig. 45). Since the pairs a, b and m, n are harmonic, the pairs A, B and M, N are also harmonic, and M is, therefore, the midpoint of AB (p. 83). If O

is the intersection of the four given lines, the triangles
AMO and *BMO* are then congruent and hence the angle
AOM is equal to the angle *BOM*.

Given any two lines through
O, one and only one pair of
bisectors as defined above
always exists. For the pairs
of lines harmonic with the
two given lines form the conjugate pairs of the involution
of which the given lines are
double lines. This involution and the involution of
perpendicular lines through *O* have one conjugate pair
in common, since the circular involution at *O* is elliptic
(p. 61).

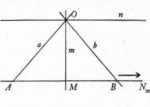

Fig. 45

35. Axes of a conic. The pairs of conjugate diameters of a central conic form an involution of lines
through the center. *This involution will, in general,
have one and only one pair in common with the circular
involution at the center* (p. 61). If two pairs of conjugate diameters of a conic are pependicular, every two
conjugate diameters are perpendicular, since in that
case the involution of conjugate diameters coincides with
the circular involution at the center (p. 56).

A conic in which the involution of conjugate diameters is circular is called a *circle*. The single pair of
perpendicular conjugate diameters of a central conic
which is not a circle are called the *axes* of the conic.

The chords of a central conic drawn perpendicular
to one of the axes are bisected by this axis (p. 88). We
may summarize the results just obtained as follows:

*A central conic which is not a circle has just one pair
of axes. The conic is symmetric with respect to either axis.*

, conj. to li at ∞

The diameters of a parabola are all parallel. One of these diameters, however, bisects the chords perpendicular to it. This diameter is called the *axis* of the parabola. *A parabola has only one axis and is symmetric with respect to its axis.*

The asymptotes of a hyperbola are evidently double lines of the involution of conjugate diameters. Hence, *the axes of a hyperbola are harmonic with the asymptotes and bisect the angles between them.*

36. Foci of a conic. If a conic be given, to every line *u* in the plane of the conic there corresponds one and only one line *u'* which is at once conjugate and perpendicular to *u*. Such a pair of lines are called *conjugate normals* with respect to the conic. In the pencil of lines through any point *P* of the plane not on the conic the pairs of conjugate lines form an involution which contains at least two conjugate lines which are perpendicular to each other (p. 61); and if it contains two pairs of perpendicular conjugate lines, all conjugate pairs consist of perpendicular lines (p. 56). If the point *P* is on the conic, it is clear that the only pair of conjugate normals through *P* is the tangent to the conic at *P* and the line through *P* perpendicular to the tangent. Hence we have established the following:

Through every point in the plane of a conic passes at least one pair of conjugate normals of the conic; if through the point pass two pairs of conjugate normals, all the pairs of conjugate lines through the point are conjugate normals.

This raises the question as to whether there exist in the plane of any conic points such that all the pairs of conjugate lines through them are conjugate normals.

Any such point is called a *focus* of the conic. We have already found such a point in the case of a special type of conic, since in the case of a circle the involution of conjugate lines through the center coincides with the orthogonal involution. Hence, *the center of a circle is a focus*. Moreover, it is easy to see that the center is the only focus of a circle.

Let us then investigate the existence of foci of a conic other than a circle. Let F be a focus. If F be joined to the center of the conic (we do not exclude the possibility that the center may be at infinity), this line will be a diameter whose pole is the point at infinity on the line through F perpendicular to the diameter. The latter is, therefore, an axis. *Every focus of a conic must then lie on an axis of the conic.*

Let a be an axis of the conic, and let P be any point of a (Fig. 46, p. 95). The polar p of P is then perpendicular to a. Let u be a variable line through P and let U be its pole, which is of course on p. Let u' be the line through U perpendicular to u, and let u' meet a in P'. We show, first, that as u rotates about P, the point P' remains fixed; i.e., u' rotates about P'. To this end we note that u' passes through the point at infinity U'_∞ which is the conjugate in the orthogonal involution of the point at infinity U_∞ on the line u. We have then (p. 78):

$$[U] \mathbin{\overline{\wedge}} [u] \mathbin{\overline{\wedge}} [U_\infty] \mathbin{\overline{\wedge}} [U'_\infty],$$

and hence the correspondence between the points U and U'_∞ is projective. The lines u' are the lines joining pairs of corresponding points of two projective pencils of points on the line p and the line at infinity. In order to show that the lines u' all pass through a fixed point it is then only necessary to show that the projectivity just considered is perspective; or, that in this projectivity the point at infinity on p is self-corresponding (p. 48). But it is at once evident that when U coincides with the point at infinity on p, the line u coincides with a, and that U'_∞ then also coincides with the point at infinity on p. The lines u', therefore, all pass through a fixed point which is on a, since a is one of the lines u'; i.e., the lines u' all pass through P' which is fixed.

Reciprocally, if we had started with u' of the pencil of lines through P', the line u would have been the conjugate normal of u' and the point P would have been obtained as the fixed point through which pass all the lines u; in other words, the correspondence between the points P and P' is a reciprocal one. We must now prove that this correspondence is also projective, and is hence an involution. We accordingly let P move on a. By what precedes the point P' is determined on a as the intersection with a of the conjugate normal of any one line u through P (distinct from a). We may then take for our lines u the lines of the pencil with center U_∞, regarded now as a fixed point on the line at infinity, the lines of this pencil meeting a in the points P. If we denote by $[u]$ the pencil of lines with center at U_∞, by $[U]$ the pencil of points described by U, the pole of u, and by $[u']$ the pencil of lines u' with center at U'_∞, the conjugate of U_∞ in the orthogonal involution, we have

$$[P] \barwedge [u] \barwedge [U] \barwedge [u'] \barwedge [P'],$$

which shows that the correspondence between P and

P' is projective.   This correspondence is then an ordinary involution and such an involution is defined on any axis of a conic by the pairs of points in which pairs of conjugate normals with respect to the conic meet the axis in question.   The involution thus established on the axis a we may call I_a.

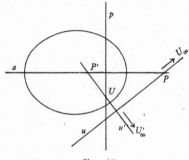

Fig. 48

It is clear that a focus F on the axis a must be a double point of the involution I_a; and, conversely, any double point of I_a is a focus of the conic on a.   Our question as to the existence of foci of a conic then depends simply on the question whether the involutions I_a, I_b on the axes a, b of a central conic or the involution I_a on the axis of a parabola are hyperbolic or elliptic.

In the case of the parabola, the point at infinity on the axis is clearly a double point of I_a.   For, in this case the line at infinity is tangent to the conic; if U_∞ is the point of contact of the line at infinity any line through U_∞ forms with the line at infinity a conjugate pair which also pass through a conjugate pair of the orthogonal involution.   The involution I_a is, therefore, hyperbolic and must have one other double point. Hence, *a parabola has a single (proper) focus on its axis.*

In the case of a central conic (ellipse or hyperbola) the situation is not quite so simple. The fact is that one of the involutions I_a, I_b is always hyperbolic and the other elliptic. A formal proof will appear presently. The reader may at this point, however, readily convince himself of this fact by the following considerations: The center C of the conic and the point at infinity on either axis evidently form a conjugate pair of the involution I_a or I_b as the case may be. If the involution on one of the axes, say a, is elliptic, any other conjugate pair of I_a must lie on opposite sides of C, since any two conjugate pairs of an elliptic involution separate each

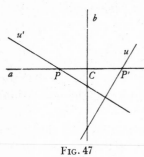

FIG. 47

other. Reference to Fig. 47 will make it clear that any pair of conjugate normals u and u' meeting a in two points on opposite sides of C must meet b in two points on the same side of C. The latter pair and the pair consisting of C and the point at infinity on b do then not separate each other, so that the involution I_b is hyperbolic. Vice versa, if I_a had been assumed hyperbolic, similar considerations would show that I_b must then be elliptic.

We conclude that *every central conic (not a circle) has two and only two (real) foci, both of which are situated on one of the axes of the conic.* The axis containing the foci is called the *principal axis* of the conic.

Since any pair of conjugate normals with respect to a conic meet the principal axis of the conic in a pair of the involution of which the foci are double points, a pair of conjugate normals through a point P in the plane of the conic are harmonic with the lines joining P to the foci of the conic (p. 56); in other words, *any pair of conjugate normals with respect to a conic bisect the angles formed by the lines joining their point of intersection to the foci of the conic* (p. 90).

In particular, *the tangent and normal to a conic at a point P of the conic bisect the angles formed by the lines joining P to the foci.*

In the case of a parabola one of the foci is at infinity, so that the last result becomes: *The tangent and normal to a parabola at a point P bisect the angles formed by the line joining P to the focus and the line through P parallel to the axis.*

We may note in closing this section that the preceding argument does not apply to a circle. In this case the two foci coincide at the center and the involutions I_a and I_b degenerate.

37. Metric property of an involution. At this point it seems desirable to abandon definitely the second method of approach to the study of metric relations referred to on p. 82 and to adopt for the remainder of this chapter the first method which assumes a knowledge of elementary euclidean geometry. This will enable us to secure very simply certain additional important metric properties which under the purely projective procedure would require an elaborate preparation and would besides make more demands on the reader's previous knowledge.

We begin by considering a certain fundamental metric relation in an involution of points on a line. Given such an involution, the conjugate of the point at infinity on the line is called the *center* of the involution. If the

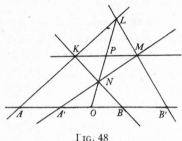

Fig. 48

involution has double points every conjugate pair is harmonic with them (p. 56). Hence, *the center of an involution is the midpoint of the segment between the double points, if such exist.*

Now let A, A' and B, B' be two conjugate pairs of an involution on a line and let the center O of the involution be constructed by the complete quadrangle $KLMN$ as in Fig. 48. If P is the intersection of KM and LN, KM being by hypothesis parallel to AA', the triangles LOB' and LPM are similar, and hence we have

$$OB':PM = LO:LP,$$

also, since the triangles NOB and NPK are similar, we have

$$OB:PK = NO:NP.$$

These relations give by multiplication

$$(OB \cdot OB'):(PK \cdot PM) = (LO \cdot NO):(LP \cdot NP).$$

By considering similarly the triangles LOA, LPK and NOA', NPM, we obtain

$$(OA \cdot OA'):(PK \cdot PM) = (LO \cdot NO):(LP \cdot NP).$$

It follows at once that we have

$$OA \cdot OA' = OB \cdot OB' = \text{a constant}.$$

This fundamental relation, which in some treatments of projective geometry is taken as the definition of an involution, may be stated in words as follows:

The product of the distances from the center to two conjugate points of an involution is constant.

If the pair A, A' are on the same side of the center O (as in Fig. 48) the segments OA and OA' will have the same direction and, hence, the constant $OA \cdot OA'$ will be positive; if the pair A, A' are on opposite sides of O the constant $OA \cdot OA'$ will be negative, and this is obviously true for every conjugate pair of a given involution. For, if U_∞ be the point at infinity on the line, every pair of an involution separates O and U_∞, or every pair does not separate O and U_∞, according as the involution is elliptic or hyperbolic (p. 57). We have here a verification of the result previously obtained as to the existence of double points of an involution. If M is a double point the relation just derived would involve the relation $\overline{OM}^2 = OA \cdot OA'$, and this will have a (real) solution OM only if $OA \cdot OA'$ is positive, i.e., if two conjugate pairs do not separate each other.

38. Construction of an involution by means of circles. The relation we have derived in the preceding section suggests another method of constructing the pairs of an involution when two pairs A, A' and B, B' are given. Through A and A' draw any circle and through B and B' draw another circle such that it meets the first circle in two points T and T'. By

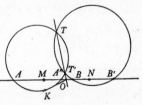

Fig. 49

a well known proposition of plane geometry we then have (Fig. 49)

$$OA \cdot OA' = OT \cdot OT' = OB \cdot OB',$$

where O is the intersection of TT' with the line of the involution. But this relation shows that O is then the center of the involution and that any other circle through T and T' and cutting the line of the involution will cut it in a pair of the involution.

To find the double points of the involution, we need only construct the tangent to one of these circles from O; if its point of contact is K, we would have $\overline{OK}^2 = OT \cdot OT'$. The two points M and N at distances equal to OK on either side of O are then the double points of the involution. The reader should note that, if the points A, A' and B, B' separate each other, the point O is necessarily inside all the circles through T and T' and that hence no tangent from O to any such circle can be drawn. This is as it should be, since in this case the involution is elliptic.

39. Construction of the foci of a central conic.. We may now return to the discussion of the foci of a central conic. We saw on p. 95 that the pairs of conjugate normals meet the axes a and b of the conic in the pairs of two involutions I_a and I_b. If either of these has double points, these double points are foci of the conic. If one of the involutions mentioned, I_a, say, is hyperbolic with double points F and F', the other involution I_b must be elliptic. For the pairs of conjugate normals at F constitute the circular involution which is elliptic and these pairs of conjugate normals meet b in the pairs of I_b. We know then that at least one of the involutions

I_a, I_b is elliptic. Let it be I_b, and let P, P' and Q, Q' be two of its conjugate pairs (which by hypothesis separate each other). Draw circles on PP' and QQ' as diameters. These circles will intersect in two points F

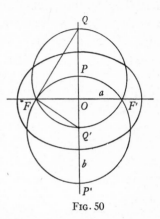

and F', and since the line FF' cuts the axis b in the center of the involution I_b and since this center is the center O of the conic, the line FF' must be the other axis a. Moreover, the lines FQ and FQ' are conjugate normals since the angle QFQ' is inscribed in a semicircle and the lines pass through

FIG. 50

Q and Q' respectively. Similarly for the lines FP and FP', and for any pair of lines which join F to a pair of the involution I_b. The two points F, F' are then the foci of the conic.

40. Metric definitions of a conic. We are now in a position to prove the well known properties of conics on which the definitions of these curves as given in elementary analytic geometry depend. We begin with the following definition:

The polar of a focus of a conic is called the *directrix* of the conic associated with that focus. The point or points in which the principal axis of a conic meets the conic are called the *vertex* or *vertices* of the conic.

The directrix is evidently perpendicular to the principal axis. In a parabola the vertex is midway between the focus and directrix, since it is the harmonic conjugate of the point at infinity on the principal axis with respect to the focus and the point in which the directrix meets the axis.

Now let F be a focus of a conic and d the corresponding directrix, and let P be any point on d (Fig. 51). Through P draw any line meeting the conic in two

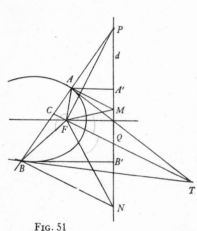

FIG. 51

points A and B, and let the tangents at A and B meet at T, the pole of AB. Since d is the polar of F, the lines FP and FT are conjugate and since they pass through the focus they must be perpendicular to each other. Let FT, the polar of P, meet AB in C. The points PC, AB then form a harmonic set (p. 76). If we project this harmonic set parallel to FT on d, we obtain the harmonic set PQ, MN. The lines FP FQ, FM FN are then a harmonic set in which the first two are at right angles to each other. Hence the angles QFM and QFN are equal. For a similar reason the angles CFA and CFB are equal. But this shows that the triangles FAM and FBN are similar, and hence the homologous sides give the following proportion:

$$FA : AM = FB : BN.$$

If through the points A and B we draw lines AA' and BB' perpendicular to the directrix this proportion becomes

$$FA:AA' = FB:BB'$$

This is one of the properties referred to at the outset which is often used as a definition of a conic: *The ratio of the distance of a point on a conic from the focus to its distance from the directrix is constant.* This ratio is called the *eccentricity* of the conic.

An ellipse or a hyperbola has two foci and two directrices; and the eccentricity, e, is of course the same for one focus and its associated directrix as for the other, since the curves are symmetric with respect to

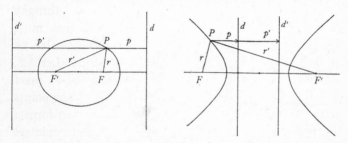

FIG. 52

both their axes (p. 91). Let r, r' represent the so-called *focal radii* of a point P on an ellipse or hyperbola, i.e., the distances of P from the foci F and F' respectively, and let p, p' be distances of P from the corresponding directrices. Then the relation just proved gives $r = ep$ and $r' = ep'$, whence we obtain $r + r' = e(p + p')$ and $r - r' = e(p - p')$. In the case of the ellipse $p + p'$ is constant, being the distance between the directrices, while in the hyperbola $p - p'$ is constant for the same reason. Hence, *in the ellipse the sum of the focal radii of any point is constant*; *in the hyperbola the difference of the focal radii of any point is constant*.

This is the other property referred to above which is often used to define the ellipse and the hyperbola. Having thus identified the curves which we defined by purely projective means in Chapter V as conics with the curves known by that name in metric geometry, we may close this part of our discussion.

CHAPTER VII

41. The symbolic representation of correspondences. In the preceding chapters we have given a systematic and thoroughly elementary account of a significant portion of projective geometry. After having given in the last chapter some of the metric specializations of projective geometry, we now return to the purely projective point of view developed in Chapters III, IV, and V. In the remaining chapters we propose to take up some of the more general aspects of our subject. The treatment from now on will be less systematic, our aim being to give an exposition of results, methods, and points of view rather than all the details of demonstrations. For this reason and also because of the fact that we shall be dealing with somewhat more advanced topics, the reader may find that the remaining chapters make a somewhat greater demand on his mathematical maturity and previous mathematical training.

Projective transformations between two pencils of points, or between two pencils of lines, the perspective correspondence between the points and lines of two planes which we had occasion to consider briefly in Chapter II, are examples of the general concept of one-to-one correspondences or transformations. It will be helpful if at this point we make ourselves familiar with a symbolic method of dealing with such correspondences. Given any system S of elements (such as the points, or the lines, or the points and lines of a plane) let there be established a one-to-one correspondence between the elements of S and the elements of some other system S', and let this correspondence or transformation be represented by T. We then say that T transforms S into S', and indicate this relation by writing $T(S) = S'$. If a is any element of S, $T(a)$ represents the corresponding element of S'.

If two transformations T_1, T_2 are applied successively to a system S, such that $T_1(S) = S'$ and $T_2(S') = S''$, the transformation which transforms S directly into S'' is called the *resultant* or the *product* of T_1 and T_2 in that order, and may be represented by the symbol $T_2 T_1$. This notation follows naturally from the relations $S'' = T_2(S') = T_2(T_1(S)) = T_2 T_1(S)$.   Similarly, for a sequence of more than two transformations. Thus the symbol $T_n \cdots T_2 T_1$ represents the resultant of applying successively the transformations T_1, T_2, $\cdots$, T_n in that order.   The order in which transformations are applied is of course material. In general $T_1 T_2$ is not the same transformation as $T_2 T_1$. If we do have $T_2 T_1 = T_1 T_2$ the two transformations are said to be *commutative*. Two projective transformations on a line, for example, are not in general commutative. But, as we shall see presently, if two projective transformations on a line have the same double points they are commutative.

If a transformation T transforms a system S into a system S', the transformation which transforms S' into S is called the *inverse* of T, and is denoted by T^{-1}; i.e., from the relation $T(S) = S'$ follows the relation $T^{-1}(S') = S$. The product of a transformation by its inverse leaves every element unchanged. This transformation is called the *identical transformation* or simply the *identity* and is denoted by the symbol 1. We have then the relations

$$TT^{-1} = T^{-1}T = 1, \quad 1T = T1 = T.$$

It is easy to see that the product of three transformations T_1, T_2, T_3 always satisfies the so-called *associative law*: $(T_3 T_2)T_1 = T_3(T_2 T_1)$. We may accordingly in any product of transformations introduce or remove parentheses at will, provided the order of the transformations is left unchanged, and we may replace any transformation in the product by a product of transformations equal to the given transformation. In particular we may note that the inverse of the product $T_2 T_1$ is $T_1^{-1}T_2^{-1}$ since we obviously have $(T_2 T_1)(T_1^{-1}T_2^{-1})$ $= T_2(T_1 T_1^{-1})T_2^{-1} = T_2 T_2^{-1} = 1$.

The resultant of a transformation T repeated n times $TTT \cdots T$ is denoted by T^n. If for some value of n we have $T^n = 1$, the smallest value of n for which this relation holds is called the *period* or the *order* of T, and T is said to be *periodic* or of *finite order*. A transformation of period 2, i.e., a transformation $T(\neq 1)$ for which $T^2 = 1$ is said to be *involutoric*. Any involutoric transformation is its own inverse, $T^{-1} = T$. An involution on a line as defined on p. 55 is an example of an involutoric transformation.

42. The concept of a group of transformations. A set of transformations such that the inverse transformation of every transformation of the set is in the set and such that the product of every two transformations of the set is also in the set is called a *group of transformations*.

If we recall the definition of a projective transformation we observe at once that the inverse of any such transformation is projective and that the product of any two is likewise projective. If then we were to consider the set consisting of all possible projectivities on a line (including the identity, of course), this set forms a group. It is known as the *general projective group* on the line.

If a transformation T transforms every element of a figure into an element of the same figure, the figure is said to be *invariant* under T. It is then clear that *the set of all transformations of a given group which leave a given figure invariant forms a group*, a so-called *subgroup* of the given group. Thus the set of all projectivities on a line which leave a given point of the line invariant forms a group, a subgroup of the general projective group on the line. Likewise the set of all projectivities on a line which leave each of two given distinct points invariant, i.e., which has the two given points as double points, forms a group.

If every two transformations of a group are commutative the group is said to be a *commutative group*. The last group given as an example is of this kind, as we will show in the next section.

43. **Two important groups of projectivities on a line.** Let M and N be two given distinct points of a line and let us consider the set of all projectivities on the line for which these two points are double points. We have just seen that this set of projectivities forms a group. Moreover, by the fundamental theorem (p. 48), there is one and only one projectivity of this group which transforms a given point A, distinct from M and N, into

another point A_1 of the line. By virtue of the latter property the group is said to be *simply transitive*. It is, moreover, a commutative group, as the following considerations will show. In the adjoining figure (Fig. 53),

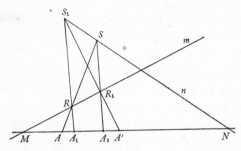

FIG. 53

we have used the usual construction (p. 53) for a projectivity with two double points M, N and have indicated the transformation T_1 of our group, which transforms the point A into A_1 by the perspectivities

$$A \underset{\wedge}{\overset{S}{=}} R \underset{\wedge}{\overset{S_1}{=}} A_1,$$

and the transformation T_2 which transforms A into A_2 by the perspectivities

$$A \underset{\wedge}{\overset{R}{=}} S \underset{\wedge}{\overset{R_1}{=}} A_2.$$

The projectivity T_2 puts A_1 through S_1 into A', while the projectivity T_1 puts A_2 through R_1 into A'. Since then T_2T_1 and T_1T_2 both put A into A', and since every projectivity of this group is completely determined by one pair of homologous elements distinct from the double points, it follows that $T_2T_1 = T_1T_2$. These considerations may be summarized as follows:

(1) *The set of all hyperbolic projectivities on a line having the same two double points forms (with the identity) a simply transitive, commutative group.*

Another group of projectivities on a line which will prove to be of fundamental importance later is described in the following:

(2) *The set of all parabolic projectivities on a line having the same double point forms (with the identity) a simply transitive, commutative group.*

The reader may consider this merely a special case of the preceding when the two double points M, N coincide. However, it is necessary to show that the product of two parabolic projectivities with the same double point M is parabolic. Let T_1 and T_2 be two such projectivities and suppose it possible that T_2T_1 has a second double point $N(\neq M)$. If T_1 transforms N into N', necessarily distinct from N, T_2 would have to transform N' into N. But this would make T_2 the inverse of T_1, and would make $T_2T_1 = 1$. The product of two transformations of our set is then parabolic, unless it is the identity. (When we speak of the set of all parabolic projectivities having a given double point we include in the set the identity. Every group must, of course, contain the identical transformation.)

That the group of parabolic projectivities under consideration is commutative may be considered as a special case of the preceding argument when the points M, N coincide. The reader may, however, find it interesting to prove it independently. The fact is that while the former proof necessarily makes use of the fundamental theorem on a line, the proof for the case of parabolic projectivities can be formulated so as to depend only on the theorem concerning quadrangular sets (p. 35) without making use of the fundamental theorem.

These two groups will be found fundamental in the next chapter in connection with the introduction of analytic methods into projective geometry without the use of any metric considerations.

44. The transformation of a correspondence. Suppose we have a correspondence T which transforms a system S into S' and suppose another transformation T_1 transforms S into S_1 and S' into S_1'. The transformation $T_1TT_1^{-1}$ then transforms S_1 into S_1'. The transformation $T_1TT_1^{-1}$ is called the *transform of T by T_1*.

Suppose, for example, that T is a projectivity on a line u and that T_1 transforms the points of u into the points of another (or the same) line u_1. The transform $T_1TT_1^{-1}$ of T then is a projectivity on u_1, such that if P, P' are two homologous points of u under T, and T_1 transforms P and P' into P_1 and P_1' respectively, the latter will be homologous under $T_1TT_1^{-1}$. In particular, if M is a double point of T and $T_1(M) = M_1$, then M_1 will be a double point of $T_1TT_1^{-1}$. It follows that the transform of any hyperbolic projectivity will be hyperbolic, the transform of any elliptic projectivity will be elliptic, and the transform of any parabolic projectivity will be parabolic.

A projectivity T_1 will transform a projectivity T into itself if and only if T and T_1 are commutative; for from $T_1TT_1^{-1} = T$, follows $TT_1 = T_1T$. It is readily seen that a projectivity T_1 will transform a group of projectivities into a set which forms a group. If T_1 transforms a group G into a group G_1, we write $T_1 G T_1^{-1} = G_1$. If $G_1 = G$, we say that T_1 *transforms G into itself*, or that *G is invariant under T_1*. If every transformation of a group G_1 transforms a group G into itself, *G_1 is said to transform G into itself*, or *G is invariant under G_1*. From what precedes it is readily seen, for example, that *the group of all hyperbolic projectivities on a line with double points M, N transforms into itself the group of all parabolic projectivities on the line with double point M*.

45. Projective transformations of two-dimensional forms. We have hitherto given but little attention to projective correspondences between the elements of two two-dimensional or two three-dimensional forms. We did have occasion once (p. 20) to consider briefly what we called a perspective correspondence between two planes. This is a special case of the following definition:

A *projective transformation* between the elements of two two-dimensional (or two three-dimensional) forms is any reciprocally one-to-one correspondence between the elements of the two forms, such that to every one-dimensional form of one there corresponds a projective one-dimensional form of the other.

We shall take as typical of two-dimensional forms the *planar field*, i.e., the points and lines of a plane. If to every point of one plane there corresponds a point of another (or the same) plane, then if the correspondence is projective as defined above, to every line of the first plane will correspond a line of the second, to every pencil of points in the first will correspond a projective pencil of points in the second, and to every pencil of lines in the first will correspond a projective pencil of lines in the second. The perspective correspondence between two planes considered earlier (p. 20) clearly satisfies these conditions. Moreover, the resultant of any sequence of such perspective correspondences will evidently also satisfy the conditions. The kind of correspondence we have just been considering, where to every element of one form corresponds an element of the same kind in the other form i.e., a point to a point, and a line to a line, is called a *collineation*, and if the correspondence is also projective, it is called a *projective collineation*. If we confine ourselves to ordinary *real* space every collineation is necessarily projective (although this is not the case if imaginary elements are present). It may be shown that every projective collineation can be obtained as the resultant of a sequence of perspectivities. In the sequel when we use the word collineation a projective collineation is meant.

If, on the other hand, we have a projective correspondence whereby to every point of one plane corresponds a line of the other and to every line of the one a point of the other, the correspondence is called a *correlation*. We have had an example of such a correlation (in which the two planes coincide) in the case of the polar system of a conic (p. 77). In a polar system to every pencil of points in the plane corresponds a projective pencil of lines, and vice-versa.

The two planes between which a collineation or a correlation establishes a correspondence may of course coincide. We then have a collineation or correlation on a plane. The inverse of any such collineation on a plane and the resultant of any two collineations on a plane are clearly collineations on the plane. The set of all possible collineations on a plane (including the identical collineation) then forms a group, the so-called *general group of collineations on the plane*. The resultant of two correlations on a plane is, however, a collineation. The set of all correlations on a plane, therefore, does not form a group. But the set of all correlations and collineations on the plane does form a group.

The fundamental theorem of projective geometry states that any projectivity between two lines is completely determined if three pairs of homologous points are given. The corresponding theorem for a collineation between two planes is as follows:

A projective collineation between two planes (or on a single plane) is uniquely determined when four pairs of homologous points are given, provided no three of either set are collinear.

That there can not be more than one collineation transforming a complete quadrangle $ABCD$ into another $A'B'C'D'$ follows readily from the fact that, if there were two, T and T_1, $T^{-1}T_1$ would leave each of the points A, B, C, D fixed. The lines joining these points in pairs would then remain fixed, and hence there would be three points on each of the sides of the triangle ABC which remain fixed. But this would imply that every point on each of these sides remains fixed and hence each of the lines through A, B, C would remain fixed. If P is any point of the plane containing ABC, two of the lines AP, BP, CP must be distinct, and since $T^{-1}T_1$ leaves each of these lines fixed, it must leave P fixed. Hence we have $T^{-1}T_1 = 1$, or $T_1 = T$.

That there exists at least one collineation transforming a quadrangle $ABCD$ into any other quadrangle $A'B'C'D'$ may be seen by actually constructing such a correspondence between the elements of the two planes. To the three lines AB, AC, AD of the pencil of lines at A must correspond the three lines $A'B'$, $A'C'$, $A'D'$ of the pencil of lines at A' and this correspondence defines uniquely a projectivity T_A between these two pencils of lines. Similarly, we establish a unique projectivity T_B between the pencils at B and B' by making the lines BA, BC, BD correspond respectively to the lines $B'A', B'C', B'D'$. To every point P not on the line AB we make correspond the intersection P' of the lines $T_A(AP)$ and $T_B(BP)$. To any line a of the first plane not passing through A or B, which may be considered as the axis of perspectivity of two perspective pencils of lines at A and B, we make correspond the axis of perspectivity of the perspective pencils at A' and B' into which T_A and T_B transform the perspective pencils at A and B, respectively. That T_A and T_B do transform the perspectivity between the pencils at A and B into a perspectivity between the pencils at A' and B' follows from the fact that to the line AB corresponds the line $A'B'^v$ under both T_A and T_B, so that in the projective correspondence between the pencils at A' and B' the line $A'B'$ is self-corresponding. To two lines of the first plane intersecting on the line AB will then correspond two lines intersecting on $A'B'$ in the second plane. Finally, to any point P of AB we make correspond the point P' of $A'B'$ determined by the line homologous to any line of the first plane passing through P. We have thus defined a reciprocally one-to-one correspondence between the two planes which satisfies the definition of a projective collineation.

If the points of a plane α be projected from a point S on a distinct plane α' and the points of α' are then projected from a different center S' back on to α, we obtain in α a correspondence H in which evidently every point of the line o of intersection of α and α' remains fixed and in which the point O in which the line SS' meets α also remains fixed. Such a correspondence on a plane in which a point O and every point of a line o remain fixed is called a *perspective collineation* on the plane. If the point O is not on the line o, the perspective collineation is called a *homology*; if the point O is on the line o, it is called an *elation*. The point O and the line o are called the *center* and the *axis* of the homology or elation, respectively.

Such perspective collineations exist with any point and any line as axis and center. Any two homologous points A, A' must evidently be collinear with O, since the line OA meeting o in some point must be invariant, and hence A' must lie on OA. Moreover, given the center O and axis o, a perspective collineation is uniquely determined by any pair of distinct homologous points collinear with O. The existence of one such perspective collineation follows readily from the fact that if we take any plane through o distinct from the given plane and any point S not on either of the two planes, a point S' is readily determined which yields the desired collineation as the resultant of two perspectivities with centers at S and S'. That there can not be more than one such perspective collineation follows from the fundamental theorem (p. 114) already proved.

The perspective collineations are, of course, a very special type of collineation in that they leave every point of a line invariant and leave every line through a point invariant. The projectivities on the lines through the center distinct from the axis are in the case of an elation all parabolic, in the case of a homology all hyperbolic. A homology of special interest is the so-called *harmonic homology* in which every pair of homologous points are harmonic with the center and the point in which the line containing the homologous pair meets the axis. A harmonic homology is evidently of period two or involutoric.

A collineation on a plane which leaves invariant as many as four points, no three of which are collinear, reduces to the identity. If a collineation leaves each of three non-collinear points invariant, it is said to be of Type I, provided it is not a homology; the projectivities on the sides of the invariant triangle are all hyperbolic. If two of the three points coincide, we obtain a collineation whose invariant figure consists of two points M, N, the line joining them, and another line through one of them. Such a collineation is said to be of Type II (if it is not an elation); the projectivity on the line joining the double points is hyperbolic and on the other invariant line parabolic. If the points M, N coincide, the invariant figure consists of a single point M and a line through it. The projectivity on the invariant line is parabolic, as is also the projectivity in the pencil of lines on the invariant point; such a collineation is said to be of Type III. Finally the homology is of Type IV, and the elation is of Type V.

46. Groups of collineations in the plane. The set

consisting of all collineations in a plane (with the identity) has already been referred to as constituting the so-called general group of collineations in the plane. An important subgroup of the general group consists of all the collineations in the plane leaving a given line invariant, the so-called *affine group*. Another group of importance is the set of all collineations that leave each of two given points invariant. This group must then leave the line joining the two points invariant and is therefore a subgroup of the affine group leaving this line invariant. The set of all elations having a given axis also forms a group which will prove to be of fundamental importance later. To prove that this set forms

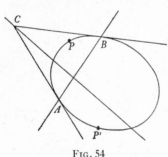

FIG. 54

a group it is necessary to prove that the resultant of any two elations of the set is an elation. We omit the proof, as the reader should have no difficulty in showing that the resultant of two such elations can not have a double point which is not on the axis.

The general group of collineations on the plane has a large number of different types of subgroups. We have called attention in the preceding to a few of these that are especially simple in their definition and are also of fundamental importance for the future. We will add to our list one more. There exist collineations leaving a conic invariant. Indeed, if A and B (Fig. 54) are two distinct points of a conic and the tangents at A

and B intersect in a point C, the harmonic homology having C for center and AB for axis evidently leaves the conic invariant (p. 76). We can easily go further, however. Any collineation must of course transform any conic into a conic, since it transforms any two projective pencils of lines into two pencils that are projective. Now it is clear that any collineation with double points A, B, C and transforming any point P of our conic into a point P' of the conic (P and P' distinct from either A or B) must transform the conic determined by the points A, B, P and the tangents at A and B into the conic determined by A, B, P' and the tangents at A and B. But the latter conic coincides with the former. *The set of all collineations leaving a given conic invariant forms a group.*

CHAPTER VIII

THE ALGEBRA OF POINTS AND THE INTRODUCTION OF ANALYTIC METHODS

47. The addition of points on a line. We propose to devote the present chapter to an exposition of one of the most interesting developments in projective geometry; viz., the introduction of analytic methods on a purely projective basis, that is, without the use of any metric notions whatever. We are so accustomed to associating magnitude with numbers, and measurement with the idea of coordinates, that it will be surprising to the uninitiated reader to learn that such metric concepts are quite unessential both to the idea of number or the idea of coordinates. This was first recognized in the field of projective geometry by VON STAUDT (1798–1867) who laid the basis for a non-metric introduction of analytic methods by his so-called *algebra of throws* (1847). We shall adopt a somewhat different point of view which is less abstract, but which of course is essentially equivalent to von Staudt's procedure.

We begin by choosing arbitrarily three distinct points on a line, which we will label 0, 1, and ∞, respectively. The reader must not attach any significance to these labels, until we prove that they have certain properties in connection with operations about to be defined which are similar to properties which we are accustomed to associate with these symbols. We could just as well have labelled our three points A, B, and C; but it will facilitate the discussion if we use 0, 1, and ∞ from the start. Also, it is convenient to denote the points of our line by the small letters of the alphabet, rather than by capitals, since we propose ultimately to think of these points as associated with numbers.

With reference to these three points we now propose to define certain operations between pairs of points on our line. For this purpose we make use of two groups of projectivities on the line which we had occasion to define in the last chapter. The first of these is the group of all parabolic projectivities on the line with double point ∞. This group is simply transitive and commutative (p. 110). If a is any point of the line ($\neq \infty$) let T_a be the projectivity of our parabolic group which transforms the point 0 into the point a, i.e., such that $T_a(0) = a$. We then define the operation of *addition* (+) on any two points a, b of the line by the relation

$$(1) \qquad a+b = T_a(b).$$

This operation associates with every pair a, b of points on the line a uniquely determined point $a+b$.

According to our definition T_0 is the identical projectivity. Hence we have $0+a=a$, for every a. Also $a+0=a$, by definition. We have, therefore,

$$(2) \qquad 0+a = a+0 = a.$$

Now let a, b, c be any three points of the line and let $T_a T_b = T_r$. We then have, from the relation $T_a T_b(c) = T_r(c)$, $a+(b+c) = r+c$. If we place $c=0$, we obtain from (2) $a+b=r$, and, therefore,

$$(3) \qquad a+(b+c) = (a+b)+c.$$

In other words, *the operation of addition satisfies the associative law.*

Since our group is commutative, we have $T_aT_b = T_bT_a$. If we operate with these equal projectivities on the point 0, we obtain at once

(4) $$a+b=b+a.$$

In other words, *the operation of addition is commutative.*

Let T_r be the inverse of T_a. Then since T_aT_r is the identity, $T_aT_r(0)=0$, or $a+r=0$. Hence, given any point $a(\neq \infty)$ there exists a point r such that $a+r=0$. We denote the point r by the symbol $-a$, and then have

(5) $$a+(-a)=0.$$

We may then define the operation of *subtraction* $(-)$ by saying that $a-b$ is the point x such that $b+x=a$. Such a point x exists for every pair a, $b(\neq \infty)$, since $(-b)+a$ satisfies the definition in view of relations (3), (4) and (5). We have, then,

(6) $$a-b=a+(-b).$$

48. The multiplication of points on a line. We have not as yet used the point 1. We do so in defining a second operation between pairs of points a, b of our line. This operation we call *multiplication* $(\cdot)$. For this purpose we make use of the group of all hyperbolic projectivities on the line having 0 and ∞ as double points. This group is also simply transitive and commutative (p. 110). Let M_a be the projectivity of this group which transforms the point 1 into any point $a(\neq 0, \infty)$, i.e., such that $M_a(1)=a$. We then define the operation of multiplication on any two points a,

b of the line by the relation

(1) $a \cdot b = M_a(b)$.

We may in the future suppress the sign of multiplication and write simply ab for $a \cdot b$. This operation associates with every pair a, $b(\neq 0, \infty)$ of points on the line a uniquely determined point ab.

The discussion now proceeds in strict analogy with the discussion of addition, the projectivities of our hyperbolic group taking the place of those of the parabolic group used for defining addition and the point 1 playing the role that the point 0 played in the previous discussion.

The reader will have no difficulty in establishing the following properties of multiplication:

(2) $1a = a1 = a$, (3) $a(bc) = (ab)c$, (4) $ab = ba$.

The last two state that *the operation of multiplication is associative and commutative*. He will also establish readily the fact, for any $a(\neq 0, \infty)$ there exists an element which we denote by a^{-1} such that

(5) $aa^{-1} = 1$.

We define the operation of *division* (/) by saying that a/b is the point x such that $bx = a$. Such a point exists for every $b(\neq 0, \infty)$, since ab^{-1} satisfies the condition, so that we have

(6) $a/b = ab^{-1}$.

In addition we have evidently $a0 = 0$, since 0 is a double point for every projectivity of our group. The symbol $0a$ has no meaning under the above definition; we define it to be equal to 0. We then have, for every $a(\neq \infty)$,

$$(7) \qquad\qquad a0 = 0a = 0.$$

49. The distributive law. The group of hyperbolic projectivities which we have used to define multiplication transforms into itself the group of parabolic projectivities which we used to define addition (p. 112). This means that if M_a is any projectivity of the former group and T_b any projectivity of the latter there exist a projectivity T_r of the parabolic group such that $M_a T_b M_a^{-1} = T_r$, or $M_a T_b = T_r M_a$. Operating with these equal projectivities on any point c, we obtain

$$a(b+c) = r + ac.$$

If we place $c = 0$, this gives $ab = r$. Hence, we have

$$a(b+c) = ab + ac,$$

the distributive law of multiplication with respect to addition.

50. The algebra of points on a line. We have now defined, with reference to three arbitrarily chosen distinct points $0, 1, \infty$ on a line, two operations, addition and multiplication, and their inverses, subtraction and division, which satisfy all the formal laws of ordinary algebra. The whole terminology of ordinary algebra, in so far at least as it is definable in terms of the four rational operations, may then be carried over and applied to this algebra of points.

As defined in the preceding sections, the elements of our algebra are the points of a line, rather than numbers in the ordinary sense. We may, however, use the preceding results to show how we may associate with every point of our line ($\neq \infty$) a number of our ordinary number-system. To this end we associate with the points 0, 1, the numbers 0 and 1. With the sequence of points $1+1$, $1+1+1$, $1+1+1+1$, $\cdots$, we associate the numbers 2, 3, 4, respectively, thus associating every positive integer with a unique point of our line. The negative integers are then associated with their corresponding points so that $(-n)+n=0$. This associates the number $1/n$ with a unique point, and also the numbers m/n with unique points, where m, n are

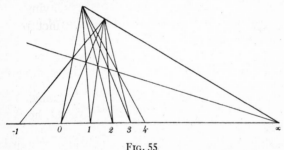

FIG. 55

any positive or negative integers. All ordinary rational numbers are then associated with points of our line in a unique way.

If the reader will make the usual construction for a parabolic projectivity with given double point (Fig. 55), he will obtain the adjoining figure for the construction of the points $2,3,4,\cdots,-1,\cdots$. Then, from the theorem of p. 54, or directly from the figure he will observe that 1 is the harmonic conjugate of ∞ with respect to 0 and 2; 2 the harmonic conjugate of ∞ with respect to 1 and 3; 3 the harmonic conjugate of ∞ with respect to 2 and

4; 0 the harmonic conjugate of ∞ with respect to 1 and
−1, etc. These considerations should make vivid for
him the way in which the process described associates
the positive and negative integers with certain definite
points of the line, the point labelled ∞ having once
been chosen and the numbers 0 and 1 having been
arbitrarily assigned to two arbitrary distinct points.
It will still further clarify the situation if we depart for
just a moment from the purely projective setting and
observe that if the point ∞ is taken as the point at
infinity on the line the points · · · , −1, 0, 1, 2, 3, 4, · · ·
will be at equal distances. This departure momentarily
from purely projective considerations should, however,
emphasize rather than obscure the fact that the definitions of our algebra of points and the resulting correspondence between the points of a line and the numbers
of algebra are built upon a purely projective foundation,
without the intervention of any metric notions what-
soever.

Having, by the preceding considerations established
a one-to-one correspondence between what may be
appropriately called the rational points of a line (with
reference to the points 0, 1, ∞) and the rational numbers, it follows readily that if we assume that the real
points of a line are ordinally equivalent to the real
numbers, the correspondence between the rational
points and the rational numbers already established
carries with it the establishment of a one-to-one
correspondence between the (real) points of a line and
the real numbers. To carry out the details of the procedure involved would require a discussion of the real
number system and a careful consideration of the

foundations of projective geometry. Such considerations seem hardly in the spirit of the present monograph, which has proceeded from the start on an intuitive foundation. From such an intuitive point of view the result reached seems sufficiently obvious without further elaboration. This result may be stated as follows:

Having chosen three distinct points of a line as the points 0, 1, ∞, *we thereby establish by the method already described a one-to-one correspondence between the real points of the line and the system of real numbers.* The *fundamental points* 0, 1, ∞ are said to establish a *scale* on the line, and the number associated with each point of the line is called the *coordinate* of the point with reference to this scale.

51. The analytic expression for a projectivity. Let a scale be established on a line; and let x' be the coordinate of the point which corresponds to the point whose coordinate is x in a projectivity on the line. We propose now to see how x' can be expressed algebraically in terms of x.

We note first that the relations

(I) $$x' = a + x \quad (a \neq \infty)$$

(II) $$x' = ax \quad (a \neq 0, \infty)$$

represent projectivities, by the definitions of the operations of addition and multiplication. Indeed, we know that (I) represents a parabolic projectivity with double point ∞; and that (II) represents a hyperbolic projectivity with double points 0 and ∞. This leads us to introduce the following properties of the exceptional symbol ∞ : $a + \infty = \infty$, and $a \cdot \infty = \infty$. Further, we may readily prove thát the relation

(III) $x' = 1/x$

represents a projectivity. For the reader will readily verify in the following figure (Fig. 56) that the definition of multiplication gives $x'x = 1$. But this construction gives at once

$$[x] \overset{A}{\barwedge} [X] \overset{1}{\barwedge} [Y] \overset{B}{\barwedge} [x'],$$

which shows that the correspondence between x and x' is projective. Moreover, it is clear that this projectivity

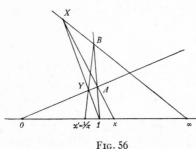

transforms the point 0 into the point ∞, and the point ∞ into the point 0. We accordingly define two more properties of the symbol ∞ : $1/0 = \infty$, $1/\infty = 0$. Also placing $x' = x$, the relation (III)

FIG. 56

gives $x^2 = 1$, which must be satisfied by any double points of the projectivity. We have, therefore, that the projectivity $x' = 1/x$ has the points 1 and -1 for double points. Clearly also this projectivity is an involution.

We may now prove the following theorem:

Any projectivity on a line is the product of projectivities of the three types (I), (II), *and* (III) *and may be expressed in the form*

(1) $x' = \dfrac{ax+b}{cx+d}.$

Conversely, every equation of this form represents a projectivity, if $ad - bc \neq 0$.

We will first prove the second half of the theorem. Let us suppose first that $c \neq 0$. We may then write equation (1) in the form

$$(2) \qquad x' = \frac{a}{c} + \frac{b - ad/c}{cx + d}.$$

This shows at once that the so-called *determinant* of the transformation, $ad - bc$, must be different from zero; for otherwise the equation would make every point x correspond to $x' = a/c$, while a projectivity must be reciprocally one-to-one. Equation (2), furthermore, shows that the correspondence established by it is the resultant of the following five:

$$
\begin{aligned}
x_1 &= cx, & x_4 &= (b - ad/c)x_3, \\
x_2 &= x_1 + d, & & \\
x_3 &= 1/x_2, & x' &= x_4 + a/c.
\end{aligned}
$$

Since each of these represents a projectivity their resultant (1) must represent a projectivity. If $c = 0$, and $ad \neq 0$, the argument is readily modified to show that (1) is the resultant of projectivities of types (I) and (II). This then proves the second half of the theorem.

It remains to show that every projectivity on the line may indeed be represented by an equation of form (1). First let us see into what point the projectivity (1) transforms the point ∞. If we follow this point through the five projectivities given above, into which (1) was resolved, we see that the first two leave it invariant, the third transforms it into 0, the fourth leaves 0 invariant while the last transforms 0 into a/c. The projectivity (1) therefore transforms ∞ into a/c. This leads us to attribute a further property to the symbol ∞; viz., *when* $x = \infty$, *we have* $(ax+b)/(cx+d) = a/c$.

According to the fundamental theorem (p. 48) a projectivity is completely determined when any three pairs of homologous points are given. Suppose that in a given projectivity the points $0, 1, \infty$ are transformed into the points p, q, r, respectively. Then it is readily verified that the transformation,

$$x' = \frac{r(q-p)x + p(r-q)}{(q-p)x + (r-q)}$$

which is of the form (1), transforms 0 into p, 1 into q, and, in view of the property just assigned to ∞, it also transforms ∞ into r. The determinant $ad - bc$ is in this case $(p-q)(q-r)(r-p)$ which is different from zero, if p, q, r are distinct. This completes the proof.

Certain corollaries should be noted:

The projectivity $x' = a/x$ $(a \neq 0, \infty)$ *transforms* 0 *into* ∞ *and* ∞ *into* 0.

This follows from the fact that the given projectivity is the resultant of the two projectivities $x_1 = 1/x$ and $x' = ax_1$. The first of these interchanges 0 and ∞, while the second leaves them both invariant. We are, therefore, led to the following definitions regarding the behavior of the symbol ∞:

$a/0 = \infty$ and $a/\infty = 0$ $(a \neq 0, \infty)$;

Any projectivity leaving the point ∞ *invariant may be expressed in the form* $x' = ax + b$;

Any double points which the projectivity (1) *may have must satisfy the equation* $cx^2 + (d-a)x - b = 0$.

The last result shows incidentally that in the real

domain there are three types of projectivities according
as this equation has two distinct real roots, two coin-
cident roots, or two conjugate imaginary roots, corresponding to the three types, hyperbolic, parabolic,
and elliptic already mentioned. We may, however, assume that our line in addition to the real points contains also points corresponding to all complex imaginary
numbers. In this complex domain there are only two
types of projectivities, according as the double points
of the projectivity are distinct or coincide. We shall
have occasion to return to these considerations later.
For the present we will still confine ourselves, as we
we have hitherto, in the main to the real domain. However, on the basis of what has just been said, we may
*think of an elliptic projectivity as one having two conjugate
imaginary double points, whenever such a conception seems
desirable.*

Before proceeding further the reader should not
neglect to observe that all the above considerations
may, under the principle of duality, be applied equally
well to the lines of a pencil of lines (or to the planes of
a pencil of planes) instead of to the points of a pencil of
points. Thus, we may construct an algebra of lines in
any pencil of lines by choosing any three distinct lines
of the pencil to be lines 0, 1, ∞, thereby establishing a
scale in a pencil of lines. The lines of the pencil may
then be put into one-to-one correspondence with the
numbers of our number system. We obtain in this
way the idea of the coordinate of any line of the pencil.
A projectivity in the pencil of lines is then represented
by equation (1), p. 128, etc.

52. **The cross ratio.** We are now in a position to

derive an expression of the greatest importance in projective geometry, an expression indeed which is often made the basis of the whole development of our subject, but which is usually derived from metric considerations. The latter procedure is undesirable, if the essential nature of projective properties is to be exhibited.

The problem leading to the introduction of this expression is as follows: By the fundamental theorem, any three distinct points of a line are projective with any three distinct points of another or the same line. If four distinct points of a line are to be made projective with four other distinct collinear points a condition must be satisfied. This condition we now propose to derive. We begin with the following definition:

If a, b, c, d are any four distinct points of a line the coordinate of the point into which d is transformed by the projectivity which transforms a, b, c respectively into ∞, 0, 1 is called the *cross ratio* of the four given points (in the given order) and is denoted by the symbol $\mathcal{R}(ab, cd)$. The same definition applies if d coincides with any one of the distinct points a, b, c. If two of the latter coincide, and d is distinct from them all, we define $\mathcal{R}(ab, cd)$ to be that one of $\mathcal{R}(ba, dc)$, $\mathcal{R}(cd, ab)$, $\mathcal{R}(dc, ba)$ for which the first three elements are distinct. This defines the cross ratio for any four points of a line of which at least three are distinct.

We may now show that the cross ratio of four points whose coordinates are a, b, c, d is given by the expression

$$\lambda = \mathcal{R}(ab, cd) = \frac{a-c}{a-d} : \frac{b-c}{b-d}.$$

For, the transformation

$$x' = \frac{a-c}{a-x} : \frac{b-c}{b-x}$$

is reducible to the form (1) of the preceding article, in which the determinant is not zero if the three points a, b, c are distinct. Moreover, it transforms a, b, c into ∞, 0, 1 respectively. Hence, it transforms $x = d$ into the given expression. If a, b, c are not all distinct we use in a similar way one of the other expressions given in the definition.

We should note, in particular, that we have $\mathcal{R}(ab, ca) = \infty$, $\mathcal{R}(ab, cb) = 0$, and $\mathcal{R}(ab, cc) = 1$, if a, b, c are any three distinct points of a line.

Also, if ab, cd form a harmonic set, we have $\mathcal{R}(ab, cd) = -1$, since we have $H(\infty, 0, 1, -1)$ by definition of -1.

It is now clear that *two sets of four points are projective, if and only if they have the same cross ratio; i.e., $abcd \;\overline{\wedge}\; a'b'c'd'$, if and only if $\mathcal{R}(ab, cd) = \mathcal{R}(a'b', c'd')$.* For, if the first four are projective respectively with ∞, 0, 1, λ, it is clear that the second four must be projective with ∞, 0, 1, λ also, if the two given sets are projective. Conversely, the relation

$$\frac{(a-c)(b-x)}{(a-x)(b-c)} = \frac{(a'-c')(b'-x')}{(a'-x')(b'-c')}$$

clearly defines a projective correspondence between x and x', which shows that if the two cross ratios are equal the two sets of four points are indeed projective.

Another way of expressing this fundamental result is to say that *the cross ratio is invariant under any projective correspondence.* The reader may, incidentally, verify this statement directly by applying to the cross ratio in turn each of the three types of projectivities (I), (II), (III) into which in a previous section (p. 127–8) we resolved any projectivity, and noting that the cross ratio remains invariant under each of these.

53. Projective correspondence between two different one-dimensional forms. So far we have considered only the analytic expression of a projectivity in a single one-dimensional form. To find such an expression for a projective correspondence between two different forms, that is between two pencils of points on different lines or between a pencil of points and a pencil of lines, for example, offers no difficulty. Let a scale be established in each of the two forms, by assigning the symbols ∞, 0, 1 to three distinct elements in each of the forms. Let x be the coordinate of any element of one of the forms and let y be the coordinate of any element of the other with reference to these two scales. The equation $y=x$ then means that two elements, one in one of the forms and the other in the other form, have the same coordinate, if y corresponds to x in the projectivity which makes the elements ∞, 0, 1 of one form correspond to the elements ∞, 0, 1 of the other. This shows that *a projectivity between the elements of two different forms can always be represented by the relation $y=x$, if the scales in the two forms are properly selected.* On the other hand, if the coordinates of the two forms are so related that $y=x$ represents a projectivity, then any projectivity between the two forms is given by the equation

$$y = \frac{ax+b}{cx+d}.$$

54. Point and line coordinates in the plane. We now turn to the problem of representing the points and lines of a plane by means of coordinates. In the case of point coordinates the reader will readily recognize the analogy of the procedure with that of elementary analytic geometry. The dual concept of line coordinates may, however, be new to him, if he is approaching the study of projective geometry for the first time.

To define the coordinates of a point in a plane we proceed as follows: Let there be given two distinct lines in the plane on each of which we establish a scale arbitrarily, except that the point O of intersection of the two lines shall be the 0 point of each scale. On one of the lines, which we will call the *x-axis*, let 1_x and $\infty_x = V$ be the other fundamental points establishing the scale,

and on the other line, which we will call the *y-axis*, let the corresponding points be denoted by 1_y and $\infty_y = U$ (Fig. 57). Then if P is any point of the plane not on UV, the line UP meets the x-axis in a

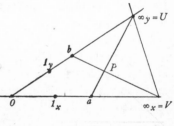

Fig. 57

unique point whose coordinate (let us say) is a, while the line VP meets the y-axis in a unique point whose coordinate on the y-scale (let us say) is b. The two numbers a, b are uniquely determined by the point P and, conversely, two such numbers, one on the x-axis and one on the y-axis uniquely determine the point P (not on UV). The two numbers a, b are called the *coordinates of the point P* and the latter is represented by the symbol (a, b), wherein the *x-coordinate* or *ab-*

scissa is always written first and the *y-coordinate* or *ordinate* is always written second. Any point of the *x*-axis has coordinates of the form $(a, 0)$ while every point of the *y*-axis has coordinates of the form $(0, b)$. The points of the line UV do not have coordinates in this system. The exceptional character of the points on the line UV will be removed presently.

The plane dual of the above considerations leads to the concept of the *coordinates of a line*. Given the pencils of lines on two distinct points U, V, we establish in each of these pencils a scale by assigning the fundamental lines ∞, 0, 1 arbitrarily, except that the line UV joining the centers of the two pencils is to be the 0 line in each scale. In the scale on U we denote the

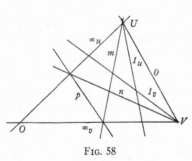

other two fundamental lines by 1_u and ∞_u, respectively; in the pencil on V, we denote these points by 1_v and ∞_v (Fig. 58). Any line p of the plane not on the intersection of the lines ∞_u and ∞_v meets the line ∞_v in a

point which determines in the pencil U a line whose coordinate in the scale on U we will call m; while it meets the line ∞_u in a point which determines in the pencil V a line whose coordinate in the V scale we will say is n. The two numbers m, n are uniquely determined by p; and conversely, two such numbers, one belonging to the U scale and one to the V scale, uniquely determine a line p. They are called the *line coordinates m, n* of the line p, and the latter may be represented by the symbol $[m, n]$, in which the u-coordinate is always written first and the v-coordinate is always written second. We have used square brackets instead of parentheses in order to distinguish the symbol representing a line from that representing a point. Every line through U has coordinates of the form $[m, 0]$,

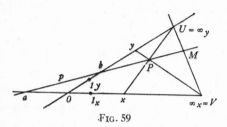

.Fig. 59

while every line through V has coordinates of the form $[0, n]$. The lines through the point O do not have coordinates in this system. The exceptional character of the lines through O will be removed presently.

55. The equation of a line. Let a line p not passing through O meet the x-axis in a point whose abscissa is a and the y-axis in a point whose ordinate is b. Let $P = (x, y)$ be any variable point of the line. If p meets the line UV in the point M (Fig. 59), we have

$$\infty_x\, 0\, a\, x \overset{U}{\overline{\wedge}} M\, b\, a\, P \overset{V}{\overline{\wedge}} \infty_y\, b\, 0\, y,$$

whence (p. 133)

$$\mathcal{R}(\infty_x 0, ax) = \mathcal{R}(\infty_y b, 0y),$$

which when expanded gives

$$\frac{x}{a} = \frac{b - y}{b} \qquad \text{or} \qquad \frac{x}{a} + \frac{y}{b} - 1 = 0.$$

Conversely, any point (x, y) whose coordinates satisfy this equation will be on the line p. This equation is accordingly called the *point equation* of the line.

If the line p passes through O, let $A = (h, k)$ be any point on it distinct from O and let as before $P = (x, y)$ be any variable point of p. If p meets UV in M (Fig. 60), we have

$$\infty_x \, 0 \, h \, x \overset{U}{\overline{\wedge}} M \, O \, A \, P \overset{V}{\overline{\wedge}} \infty_y \, 0 \, k \, y,$$

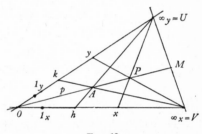

Fig. 60

whence (p. 133)

$$\mathcal{R}(\infty_x 0,\, h\,x) = \mathcal{R}(\infty_y 0,\, k\,y),$$

which when expanded gives $x/h = y/k$.

This then is the equation of any line through the origin O.

Dual considerations lead to the notion of the *line equation* of a point ; i.e., the equation which is satisfied by the coordinates u, v of all lines through the point and by no others.

56. Simultaneous point and line coordinates. The results of the last article can be given an especially symmetric and illuminating form by superimposing our systems of point and line coordinates in an appropriate way. To this end, given a set of point coordinates, i.e., an x-axis and a y-axis with a scale on each as previously described, let us place the U-center of a system of line coordinates at the point $U = \infty_y$ and the V-center at the point $V = \infty_x$, and let the line u_∞ coincide with the y-axis and the line v_∞ coincide with the x-axis. Our system of line coordinates is now completely established, except that the lines 1_u and 1_v have not yet been chosen. If we choose for 1_u the line through U and the point -1_x on the x-axis, and let T represent the projectivity which makes every line through U correspond to that point on the x-axis which has the same coordinate, and if T' represents the perspectivity whereby to every line through U corresponds the point on the x-axis in which it meets the x-axis, the projectivity $T'T$ transforms the x-axis into itself and interchanges 0 and ∞_x, and also interchanges 1_x and -1_x. Hence, $T'T$ is the involution $x' = -1/x$. It follows that with this arrangement of the two systems of coordinates *the line through U whose coordinate is u meets the x-axis in the point whose coordinate is $-1/u$; and the point on the x-axis whose coordinate is x lies on the line through U whose coordinate is $-1/x$.*

Similarly, if we choose for the line 1_v the line through V which meets the y-axis in the point whose coordinate is -1_v, *the line through V whose coordinate is v meets the y-axis in the point whose coordinate is $-1/v$; and the point on the y-axis whose coordinate is y lies on the line through V whose coordinate is $-1/y$.*

The line p, discussed in the last article, which does not pass through O and which meets the x-axis and the y-axis in points whose coordinates are a and b, respectively, is then the line whose coordinates $[m, n]$ are given by

$m = -1/a$, $n = -1/b$. Substituting these values in the equation of this line we obtain: *The point equation of the line* $[m, n]$ *is* $mx + ny + 1 = 0$. The plane dual of this result states: *The line equation of the point* (a, b) *is* $au + bv + 1 = 0$. These two statements may be combined into one:

The necessary and sufficient condition that the point (a, b) *be on the line* $[m, n]$ *is that* $ma + nb + 1 = 0$.

57. Homogeneous coordinates on the line and in the plane.   The coordinates which we have defined for the points of a line and those which we have introduced for the points and lines of a plane, are not altogether satisfactory for the analytic representation of projective elements. The reader will recall that, in the case of the coordinates on a line, the point ∞ was exceptional, so that we had to define certain special properties for it (p. 128f), whereas there should not be exceptional points. Also in the plane, the points on the line UV and the lines through the point O proved exceptional with reference to our coordinate systems. We propose now to modify our notion of coordinates in such a way as to avoid these difficulties.

Beginning with the coordinates on a line, we replace the coordinate x of any point of the line distinct from ∞, by two coordinates x_1, x_2 such $x = x_1/x_2$. Any point of the line is then represented by two coordinates (x_1, x_2) with the understanding that $(kx_1, kx_2) = (x_1, x_2)$ for every $k \neq 0$. The point ∞ is represented by the symbol $(1, 0) = (k, 0)$. The fundamental points of the scale are $0 = (0, 1)$, $1 = (1, 1)$, $\infty = (1, 0)$. A projectivity is represented by the equations:

$$\rho x_1' = ax_1 + bx_2,$$
$$\rho x_2' = cx_1 + dx_2. \qquad (ad - bc \neq 0)$$

The point $(0, 1)$ is transformed into the point (b, d) and the point $(1, 0)$ into the point (a, c), as they should be. The exceptional character of the point ∞ disappears in this new method of representing the points on a line. The coordinates (x_1, x_2) are called *homogeneous coordinates* on the line, to distinguish them from those previously used, and which will from now on be referred to as *non-homogeneous*.

A similar device serves in the plane. Given any system of simultaneous point and line coordinates as described in the last article, we replace the symbol (x, y) representing a point not on UV by a symbol (x_1, x_2, x_3) such that $x:y:1 = x_1:x_2:x_3$. To the point $V = \infty_y$ we assign the symbol $(0, 1, 0)$, to $U = \infty_x$ the symbol $(1, 0, 0)$ and to the point in which the line joining O to the point $(1, 1)$ meets UV (Fig. 61) the symbol $(1, 1, 0)$. Any other point not on UV, which in the previous system had coordinates (a, b) is joined to O by a line whose equation is (p. 138) $x/y = a/b$. This justifies us in assigning to the point in which this line meets UV the symbol $(a, b, 0)$. Every point in the plane has now been assigned a set of three numbers (x_1, x_2, x_3) with the understanding that the point $(x_1, x_2, x_3) = (kx_1, kx_2, kx_3)$ for every $k \neq 0$. Conversely, any three numbers (x_1, x_2, x_3), with the exception of $(0, 0, 0)$, define uniquely a point in the plane. This new system of coordinates is called a system of *homogeneous point coordinates* in the plane; the previous system will in the future be referred to as *non-homogeneous*. The considerations dual to those above give rise to a system of *homogeneous line coordinates* in the plane, whereby to every line of the plane corresponds a symbol $[u_1, u_2, u_3]$, and where the lines through O, which were exceptional in the non-homogeneous system, are characterized simply by the fact that for any such line we have $u_3 = 0$.

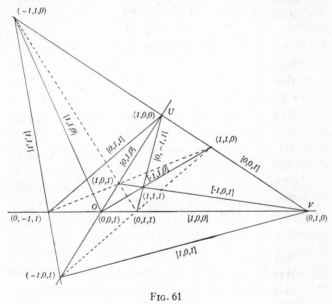

FIG. 61

The reader should note that the various points and lines used to establish a system of homogeneous coordinates in the plane now enter very symmetrically. The so-called *frame of reference* of such a system now consists of a triangle OUV, the sides of which have the equations $x_1 = 0$, $x_2 = 0$, $x_3 = 0$ and the vertices of which, in line coordinates, have the equations $u_1 = 0$, $u_2 = 0$, $u_3 = 0$. The unit point $(1, 1, 1)$ of the system, which may be any point not on a side of OUV, determines the points $(0, 1, 1)$, $(1, 0, 1)$ and $(1, 1, 0)$ on the sides of OUV. The unit line $[1, 1, 1]$ is then uniquely determined as the line on which lie the points $(-1, 1, 0)$, $(-1, 0, 1)$ and $(0, -1, 1)$ (that these points all lie on a line follows from the fact that it is the axis of perspectivity of the perspective triangle OUV and that formed of the unit points on the sides of OUV, which are evidently perspective from the point $(1, 1, 1)$).

The equation of a line $[m, n]$ not on O, which in non-homogeneous coordinates has the equation $mx + ny + 1 = 0$, becomes in homogeneous coordinates $m_1x_1 + m_2x_2 + m_3x_3 = 0$, where $[m_1, m_2, m_3]$ are the homogeneous coordinates of the line. Indeed, *the necessary and sufficient condition that the point (a_1, a_2, a_3) be on the line $[m_1, m_2, m_3]$ is that $m_1a_1 + m_2a_2 + m_3a_3 = 0$.*

The perfect symmetry of this result is all that could be desired. We may see herein a reflection of the principle of duality, since as a matter of fact the point coordinates and the line coordinates are in no way distinguishable one from the other; that is, we may in any analytic discussion interchange point and line coordinates without affecting the validity of the discussion.

The reader familiar with the theory of determinants will readily see that *the equation of the line joining the two points $A = (a_1, a_2, a_3)$ and $B = (b_1, b_2, b_3)$ is*

$$\begin{vmatrix} x_1 & x_2 & x_3 \\ a_1 & a_2 & a_3 \\ b_1 & b_2 & b_3 \end{vmatrix} = 0,$$

and that the coordinates of this line are

$$\left(\begin{vmatrix} a_2 & a_3 \\ b_2 & b_3 \end{vmatrix}, \begin{vmatrix} a_3 & a_1 \\ b_3 & b_1 \end{vmatrix}, \begin{vmatrix} a_1 & a_2 \\ b_1 & b_2 \end{vmatrix} \right)$$

Similar relations hold for the equation of the point of intersection of two lines $m = [m_1,\ m_2,\ m_3]$ and $n = [n_1,\ n_2,\ n_3]$.

As an application of these results the reader may find it interesting to verify the theorem of Desargues (p. 34) analytically. To this end we may let one of the triangles, say $A'B'C'$, be the triangle of reference: $A' = (0, 0, 1)$, $B' = (0, 1, 0)$, $C' = (1, 0, 0)$; and we may let the center of perspectivity of the two triangles be $P = (1, 1, 1)$. The point A of the other triangle ABC must then lie on the line PA', i.e., the line whose equation is $x_1 - x_2 = 0$. We may then place $A = (1, 1, a)$, where a is arbitrary. Similarly, we place $B = (1, b, 1)$, and $C = (c, 1, 1)$. We then obtain, by applying the formulas just derived and their duals, the following:

The coordinates of the line $A'B'$ are $[1, 0, 0]$;

The coordinates of the line AB are $[1 - ab, a - 1, b - 1]$.

Hence the coordinates of their intersection C'' are

$$C'' = (0,\ 1 - b,\ a - 1).$$

Similarly,

$$A'' = (1 - c,\ b - 1,\ 0) \quad \text{and} \quad B'' = (c - 1,\ 0,\ 1 - a).$$

The determinant of these three points will be found to be zero, which verifies the fact that they are collinear.

58. Pencils of points and lines. The following method of representing the points and the lines of pencils of points and lines is convenient:

If $A = (a_1,\ a_2,\ a_3)$ and $B = (b_1,\ b_2,\ b_3)$ are any two distinct points of a pencil	If $m = [m_1, m_2, m_3]$ and $n = [n_1, n_2, n_3]$ are any two distinct lines of a pencil

of points, any point P of the pencil is given by	of lines, any line p of the pencil is given by

$$P = (\lambda_2 a_1 + \lambda_1 b_1, \ \lambda_2 a_2 + \lambda_1 b_2, \qquad p = [\mu_2 m_1 + \mu_1 n_1, \ \mu_2 m_2 + \mu_1 n_2,$$

$$\lambda_2 a_3 + \lambda_1 b_3), \qquad\qquad\qquad \mu_2 m_3 + \mu_1 n_3],$$

where λ_1/λ_2 is an arbitrary parameter. | *where μ_1/μ_2 is an arbitrary parameter.*

The proof (of the result on the left) follows from the fact that any point (x_1, x_2, x_3) of the pencil must satisfy the relation

$$\begin{vmatrix} x_1 & x_2 & x_3 \\ a_1 & a_2 & a_3 \\ b_1 & b_2 & b_3 \end{vmatrix} = 0.$$

Three numbers ρ, λ_1', λ_2' then exist such that we have

$$\rho x_i = \lambda_2' a_i + \lambda_1' b_i \quad (i = 1, \ 2, \ 3).$$

The number ρ is not zero, for if so it would follow from the last relation that $a_1 : a_2 : a_3 = b_1 : b_2 : b_3$, which would make the points A and B coincide. Hence, if we place $\lambda_1 = \lambda_1'/\rho$ and $\lambda_2 = \lambda_2'/\rho$, we see that every point of the pencil may be represented in the manner indicated. Conversely, every point of this form is evidently a point of the pencil.

The method of representing the elements of a pencil just given is known as the *parametric* method of representation, in which the points A, B (the lines m, n) are called the *base points* (*base lines*). The parameter λ_1/λ_2 may also be written in non-homogeneous form $\lambda_1/\lambda_2 = \lambda$, which for some purposes is more convenient. If so written the point P is represented by

$$P = (a_1 + \lambda b_1, \ a_2 + \lambda b_2, \ a_3 + \lambda b_3).$$

In the former method of writing the parameter the points A and B correspond to the values $\lambda_1 = 0$ and $\lambda_2 = 0$, respectively; in the latter method the points A and B correspond to the values $\lambda = 0$ and $\lambda = \infty$, respectively. Since to each value of λ corresponds one point of the pencil, and conversely, we may speak of the point λ (or in the case of a pencil of lines, of the line μ).

The condition that the point λ of a pencil of points lie on the line μ of a pencil of lines is given by the equation

$$\sum (m_i + \mu n_i)(a_i + \lambda b_i) = 0.$$

When expanded this equation turns out to be of the form

$$C\mu\lambda + D\mu - A\lambda - B = 0,$$

where the coefficients A, B, C, D depend only on the coordinates of the base points and base lines of the pencils and not on the parameters of the other points of the pencil. The last relation may be written in the form

$$\mu = \frac{A\lambda + B}{C\lambda + D}.$$

This is the condition that a pencil of points and a pencil of lines be perspective. Since every projective correspondence between two one-dimensional forms can be obtained as the resultant of a sequence of perspectivities and, since the resultant of two linear fractional transformations of the above form is again of this form, we have proved the following theorem:

Any projective correspondence between the elements of two one-dimensional forms may be represented by a relation

$$\mu = \frac{\alpha\lambda + \beta}{\gamma\lambda + \delta} \qquad (\alpha\delta - \beta\gamma \neq 0)$$

between the parameters of the two forms.

The same relation, of course, represents a projectivity in any one-dimensional form if μ and λ represent corresponding values of the parameter of the form.

If the two forms are different, the general relation above may be greatly simplified by an appropriate choice of the base elements. Let us take the case of two pencils of points on distinct lines as typical, and let A and B be the arbitrarily chosen base points of one of the pencils. Choose as base points of the other pencil the points A' and B', homologous in the given projectivity to A and B, respectively. Then to the values $\lambda = 0$ and $\lambda = \infty$ must correspond the values $\mu = 0$ and $\mu = \infty$. The general projective relation of the above theorem then reduces to the form $\mu = k\lambda$.

59. The equation of a conic. We will make use of the considerations in the last article to derive the equation of a conic. If $m = m_1x_1 + m_2x_2 + m_3x_3 = 0$ and $n = n_1x_1 + n_2x_2 + n_3x_3 = 0$ are the equations of two distinct lines, the equation of any line of the pencil determined by m and n is of the form $m + \lambda n = 0$. Let a conic be generated by two projective pencils, in which the line m of one corresponds to the line p of the other, while the line n of the first corresponds to the line q of the second. The two pencils are then represented by

$$m + \lambda n = 0 \quad \text{and} \quad p + \mu q = 0,$$

where $p=p_1x_1+p_2x_2+p_3x_3$ and $q=q_1x_1+q_2x_2+q_3x_3$. The projectivity generating the conic is given by $\mu=k\lambda$. To obtain the equation of the conic we need only eliminate μ, λ between the last three relations. This gives us as the desired relation

$$np-kmq=0,$$

which when expanded is evidently an equation of the second degree in x_1, x_2, x_3.

If two tangents to a given conic be taken as two sides $x_1=0$ and $x_3=0$ of the triangle of reference of the coordinate system and the line joining their points of contact is taken as the third side $x_2=0$, the equation of the conic assumes the simple form $x_2^2-kx_1x_3=0$; if in addition a point of the conic other than one of the two points of contact is chosen as the point $(1, 1, 1)$ the equation becomes simply $x_2^2-x_1x_3=0$.

60. Collineations in a plane. We will close this chapter by indicating briefly how any projective collineation may be represented analytically. To this end we consider the general linear homogeneous transformation on the coordinates of the points in a plane:

$$\rho x_1'=a_{11}x_1+a_{12}x_2+a_{13}x_3,$$
(1)
$$\rho x_2'=a_{21}x_1+a_{22}x_2+a_{23}x_3,$$
$$\rho x_3'=a_{31}x_1+a_{32}x_2+a_{33}x_3.$$

Such a transformation evidently transforms any point (x_1, x_2, x_3) into a unique point (x_1', x_2', x_3'). It will, reciprocally, make (x_1', x_2', x_3') the correspondent of a unique point (x_1, x_2, x_3) if the determinant of the transformation,

$$A = \begin{vmatrix} a_{11} & a_{12} & a_{13} \\ a_{21} & a_{22} & a_{23} \\ a_{31} & a_{32} & a_{33} \end{vmatrix},$$

is not zero; for, the above equations can then be solved uniquely for (x_1, x_2, x_3) in terms of (x_1', x_2', x_3'). Further it is readily seen that our transformation transforms any line of the plane into a line of the plane. Finally, the transformation transforms any pencil of lines into a projective pencil. For, if it transforms the lines $m = 0$ and $n = 0$ into two lines whose equations are respectively $m' = 0$ and $n' = 0$, it is clear that it will transform the line $m + \lambda n = 0$ into the line $m' + \lambda n' = 0$, and this relation between these two pencils has been shown to be projective (p. 147).

Any transformation (1) with the restriction $A \neq 0$ then represents a projective collineation in the plane. Conversely, every projective collineation in the plane can be represented in this form. To prove this, we need only show that the vertices of a complete quadrangle can, by such a transformation, be transformed into the vertices of any other complete quadrangle. But it is a simple algebraic exercise to show that if the points $(0, 0, 1)$, $(0, 1, 0)$, $(1, 0, 0)$, and $(1, 1, 1)$ are to correspond to the points (a_1, a_2, a_3), (b_1, b_2, b_3), (c_1, c_2, c_3), and (d_1, d_2, d_3) respectively forming a complete quadrangle, then the coefficients a_{ij} of the transformation are uniquely determined (except, of course, for a factor of proportionality).

If the line $x_3 = 0$ is left invariant by our collineation we must evidently have $a_{31} = a_{32} = 0$. If this line is the exceptional line of our system of non-homogeneous coordinates $x = x_1/x_3$ and $y = x_2/x_3$, we obtain the following result which will prove to be of use in the next chapter:

If the exceptional line of a system of non-homogeneous coordinates in a plane is left invariant by a collineation, the latter is represented by

$$x' = a_1 x + b_1 y + c_1,$$
$$y' = a_2 x + b_2 y + c_2. \qquad (a_1 b_2 - a_2 b_1 \neq 0)$$

CHAPTER IX

GROUPS AND GEOMETRIES

61. A geometry defined by a group of transformations. FELIX KLEIN in his well known *Erlanger Programm* of 1872, entitled *Vergleichende Betrachtungen über neuere geometrische Forschungen*, laid down a fundamental principle which has since become classic in geometry. This principle states that given any group G of transformations (on geometric elements) the body of definitions and theorems which express properties that are left unchanged under the transformations of G (but which are not invariant under the transformations of any other group containing G) is called the *geometry associated with* or *defined by* G. Thus plane projective geometry is the geometry defined by the group of all projective collineations in the plane, because the body of definitions and theorems of plane projective geometry express properties which are invariant under the general group of projective collineations in a plane. Such properties are very general; they do not include the familiar notions of parallelism, perpendicularity, equality of distances and angles, etc. of elementary euclidean geometry, since these properties are not invariant under the general projective group. These more special properties are invariant under more restricted groups. They are all invariant, e.g. under the group of all displacements in the plane.

Any displacement or motion in the plane is represented analytically by the equations

$$x' = x \cos \theta - y \sin \theta + h,$$
$$y' = x \sin \theta + y \cos \theta + k,$$

in an ordinary system of rectangular coordinates. These equations show that the group of displacements is contained in the group of all projective collineations as a subgroup; it is indeed a subgroup of the group of collineations leaving a given line invariant (p. 150). It is, of course, evident that, in general, the more restricted the group the more properties will appear that are invariant. This suggests the problem of studying the geometries associated with each of the subgroups of the general projective group in the plane, and among these geometries we should, by what has been said, expect to find the elementary euclidean geometry. The fact is, however, that what is usually understood by the term euclidean geometry is a mixture of several geometries in the strict sense of the definition as given above. It would be interesting to consider in detail some of the more important subgroups of the general projective group and the geometries defined by them, and thereby to see precisely to what subgroup any given theorem of euclidean geometry belongs. This is, however, too ambitious a program for a brief monograph. The interested reader may be referred for a more systematic and more complete exposition of this point of view to Veblen and Young, *Projective Geometry*, Vol. II. Here we can only hope to give an outline of some of the principal results of such a study, and thus supplement the discussion of metric properties which we gave

in Chapter VI. Nevertheless, we hope that enough will
here be said to make clear to the reader the point of view
involved and to show him at least in a few instances
the group to which certain of the familiar concepts of
elementary euclidean geometry belong. We shall also
see how the two principal so-called non-euclidean
geometries arise from the group-theoretic point of view
here adopted.

62. **The affine group. The affine geometry.** We will
begin our discussion with the group of all collineations
in a plane which leave a given line invariant and which
we have already defined (p. 118) as the *affine group*.
The corresponding geometry is called the *affine geometry* (in the plane). Let the line which is left invariant
by every collineation of our group be called the *line at
infinity* and let it be denoted by l_∞. The reader should
note that this is a definition; the line l_∞ is *any* line in
the plane. It should not be thought of as necessarily
"at infinity"; only if he desires the resulting geometry
to be intuitionally equivalent to the ordinary elementary geometry, i.e., if he desires the figures of the
geometry to "look like" the figures he is familiar with,
is it necessary for him to think of l_∞ as being at infinity.

The points of l_∞ are called *points at infinity* or *ideal*
or *improper* points; the points not on l_∞ are then called
ordinary points, and the lines of the plane exclusive of
l_∞ are called *ordinary lines*. The ordinary points and
lines of the plane constitute the *euclidean plane*, and in
the rest of this monograph the word "point" when un-
modified will mean an ordinary point.

The fundamental theorem for the affine group here
given without proof is as follows: *There is one and only*

*one transformation of the affine group which transforms
the vertices A, B, C of a triangle respectively into the vertices A', B', C' of any other triangle.* We have already
seen (p. 150) that in any system of non-homogeneous
coordinates in which l_∞ is taken as the exceptional line
any affine collineation is represented by the equations

$$x' = a_1x + b_1y + c_1, \quad \text{where } \Delta = \begin{vmatrix} a_1 & b_1 \\ a_2 & b_2 \end{vmatrix} \neq 0.$$
$$y' = a_2x + b_2y + c_2,$$

We now proceed to make a number of definitions
which are the same as those given in the early part
of Chapter VI and which need not all therefore be repeated in detail: Two ordinary lines not meeting in an
ordinary point are said to be *parallel* and the pair of
lines is said to be *parallel*. A simple quadrangle $ABCD$
such that the side AB is parallel to CD and BC is parallel
to DA is called a *parallelogram*, of which the lines AC
and BD are the *diagonals*. The following theorem is an
immediate consequence of these definitions and projective theorems:

*In a euclidean plane two distinct points determine one
and only one line; two lines meet in a point or are parallel;
two lines parallel to a third line are parallel to each other;
through a given point not on a given line there is one and
only one line parallel to the given line.*

The classification of conics into *hyperbola,- parabola,*
and *ellipse*; the definition of *center, diameter, central
conics, asymptotes* (of a hyperbola) are all concepts belonging to the affine geometry, though meaningless in
general projective geometry. We now proceed to develop certain new concepts of the affine geometry.

63. The group of translations. Any elation (p. 116)

having l_∞ as its axis is called a *translation*. If l is an ordinary line through the center of the translation, the latter is said to be *parallel* to l.

We have already observed that the set of all translations forms a group. It is moreover evident that *the group of translations is invariant* (p. 108) *under the affine group*. The reader will have no difficulty in noting that every translation transforms any ordinary line into a parallel line and that it transforms each of a certain system of parallel lines into itself. Also it follows readily from the definition of a translation that *there is one and only one translation carrying a point A to any point B*.

Two figures are said to be *parallel-congruent* if they are homologous under a translation. Later we shall give a more general definition of congruence. But this restricted definition expresses a property that is invariant under the affine group and, therefore, belongs to affine geometry. That the property is invariant under the affine group follows readily from the fact that the group of translations is transformed into itself by the affine group.

The necessary and sufficient condition that the ordered point pairs AB and CD be parallel-congruent, if C is not on the line AB, is that $ABCD$ form a parallelogram. If C is on the line AB and P_∞ is the point at infinity on AB, the desired condition is that the parabolic projectivity on AB with double point P_∞ which transforms A into C shall transform B into D.

The first part of this theorem follows at once from the construction of the translation which transforms A into C (Fig. 62). The line AC is invariant and, if P_∞

is the point at infinity on AB, the line AB is transformed into CP_∞. Hence, B is transformed into the intersection D of the lines CP_∞ and the line BM_∞ joining B to the center of the translation M_∞. Under these conditions $ABDC$ is a parallelogram. The second part of the theorem follows from the fact that the projectivity on every invariant line of the translation is parabolic (p. 117) with double point at infinity.

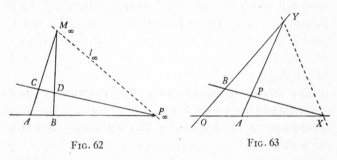

FIG. 62   FIG. 63

The last part of the theorem gives us the following as a special case:

If A and B are any two distinct points and M is the harmonic conjugate with respect to A and B of the point at infinity on the line AB, the ordered pair AM is parallel-congruent to the ordered pair MB.

This theorem suggests the definition of *midpoint* already given (p. 84). The proposition that the line joining the mid-points of two sides of a triangle is parallel to the third side and the theorem that the medians of a triangle meet in a point (p. 86–7) are then seen to be theorems belonging to the affine geometry. A similar remark applies to the proposition that the diagonals of a parallelogram bisect each other and to the theorems concerning the midpoints of parallel chords of a conic, etc. previously proved in Chapter VI (p. 88).

If OX and OY are two nonparallel lines and T is any translation, there exists a unique pair of translations T_1, T_2, such that T_1 is parallel to OX, T_2 is parallel to OY, and $T_1T_2 = T$.

To prove this theorem let T transform O into P and let the lines through P parallel to OY and OX meet OX and OY in the points A and B respectively (Fig. 63). Then, if T_1 is the translation transforming O into A and T_2 is the translation transforming O into B, it follows readily from preceding results that we have $T_1T_2 = T$. That the pair T_1, T_2 is unique follows without difficulty.

We use the last theorem to derive an analytic representation for a translation. In a non-homogeneous coordinate system for which l_∞ is the exceptional line, it is clear that any translation parallel to the x-axis is represented by the equations $x' = x+a$, $y' = y$; for the first of these equations represents any parabolic projectivity on the x-axis of the kind desired, by the definition of addition, while the second equation insures the fact that every line parallel to the x-axis is transformed into itself. Similarly, any translation parallel to the y-axis is given by equations $x' = x$, $y' = y+b$. The resultant of these two evidently yields the result expressed in the following theorem:

With respect to any non-homogeneous coordinate system for which l_∞ is the exceptional line, any translation is represented by the equations

$$x' = x+a,$$
$$y' = y+b.$$

This shows incidentally that *the group of translations is commutative*.

64. Vectors. There is another important group of concepts belonging to the affine geometry which we will define before closing this part of our discussion. The *vector AB* is a symbol which is uniquely defined for every ordered point pair AB of a euclidean plane, such that, if CD is any ordered point pair parallel-congruent to AB, the *vector CD* is equal to the *vector AB*. If A and B coincide, the vector AB is called the *null vector* and is denoted by 0.

We denote the vector AB by $V(AB)$. Since any point of a euclidean plane can be transformed into any other point of the plane by a translation, the set of all vectors is obtained as the set of all vectors of the form $V(OP)$ where O is any fixed point of the plane and P is variable.

If O, A, C are any three points of the plane, $V(OC)$ is called the *sum* of $V(OA)$ and $V(AC)$; in symbols, $V(OC) = V(OA) + V(AC)$. Since we evidently have $V(AB) + V(BA) = 0$, we define $V(BA)$ to be the *negative* of $V(AB)$, and write $V(BA) = -V(AB)$. Two vectors are said to be *collinear*, if and only if they are equal respectively to two vectors $V(OA)$ and $V(OB)$, where O, A, B are collinear points.

The sum of two non-collinear vectors OA and OB is the vector OC, where C is such that OACB is a parallelogram. This follows from the definition and the fact that $V(AC) = V(OB)$.

If O, A, B are collinear, let P_∞ be the point at infinity on the line OA and let L_∞ and M_∞ be any other two distinct points on l_∞; let the lines OL_∞ and AM_∞ meet in a point L and let BL_∞ and LP_∞ meet in M (Fig. 64). If

MM_∞ meets OA in C, $OBML$ and $ACML$ are parallelograms, so that $V(OB) = V(LM) = V(AC)$. Hence, by definition, we have $V(OA) + V(OB) = V(OC)$. But the construction just given for the point C shows that it is the sum of the two points A and B in any algebra on OA for

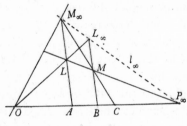

Fig. 64

which O is the point 0 and P_∞ the point ∞. This proves that *the addition of collinear vectors issuing from a point O is equivalent to the addition of the end points of the vectors in any point algebra for which O is the zero point and the point at infinity on OA is the point ∞.*

It is readily seen, moreover, that *the addition of vectors is associative and commutative*; i.e., *if a, b, c are vectors then $(a+b)+c = a+(b+c)$ and $a+b = b+a$.*

The *ratio*, OA/OB, of two collinear vectors OA and OB is the number which corresponds to A in the scale determined by $O = 0$, $B = 1$, and $P_\infty = \infty$, where P_∞ is the point at infinity on OA. With respect to an arbitrary *unit vector* OB, the ratio OA/OB of collinear vectors is called the *magnitude* of $V(OA)$. The magnitude of $V(OA)$ is clearly the same as the coordinate of A in the scale determined as above. If a_i is the magnitude of $V(OA_i)$, we have evidently *magnitude of $V(A_1A_2)$*

$= a_2 - a_1$. This gives us at once (p. 132) the following theorem:

If A_1, A_2, A_3, A_4, are four collinear points,

$$\mathcal{R}(A_1A_2,\ A_3A_4) = \frac{A_1A_3}{A_1A_4} : \frac{A_2A_3}{A_2A_4} \cdot$$

If $A_1 = A_\infty$ is the point at infinity on the line, we have

$$\mathcal{R}(A_\infty A_2,\ A_3A_4) = \frac{A_2A_4}{A_2A_3} \cdot$$

As an application of this result we may prove the following:

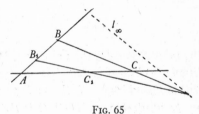

Fig. 65

If two triangles ABC and $A'B'C'$ are such that the sides AB, BC, CA are parallel, respectively, to $A'B'$, $B'C'$, $C'A'$, we have

$$\frac{AB}{A'B'} = \frac{BC}{B'C'} = \frac{CA}{C'A'} \cdot$$

This special case of a well-known theorem belongs to the affine geometry. To prove it we need only note that the translation which transforms A' into A, will transform B' into B_1 and C' into C_1, where B_1 and C_1 are points of AB and AC respectively. We then have

$$B_\infty A B B_1 \overline{\wedge} C_\infty A C C_1,$$

whence $\mathcal{R}(B_\infty A,\ BB_1) = \mathcal{R}(C_\infty A,\ CC_1)$, or AB/AB_1 $= AC/AC_1 = CA/C_1A$, which gives by definition $AB/A'B' = CA/C'A'$. A similar argument establishes the rest of the theorem.

Since the magnitudes of vectors as defined are numbers we may compute with them according to the laws of algebra. Moreover, no confusion will arise, if we denote the magnitude of the vector AB simply by the symbol AB; the ratio of two vectors is simply the quotient of their magnitudes.

We will close this part of the chapter by deriving very simply a general theorem regarding projectivities, a special case of which we derived earlier by other methods. In order to state this theorem we need the following definition: If T is any projectivity between the points of the two lines l and l', and if the points I and J' which are homologous under T^{-1} and T with the points at infinity on l' and l respectively are ordinary points, I and J' are called the *vanishing points* of l and l', respectively. The lines l and l' may coincide. The theorem in question is as follows:

If I and J' are the vanishing points on l and l' respectively of a projectivity T between the points of two parallel lines l and l', and if P is a variable point of l and $P' = T(P)$ is the corresponding point of l', the product $IP \cdot J'P'$ is constant. This constant is called the *power* of the projectivity.

The proof is as follows: Let P_∞ be the point at infinity on l and l', let P_1 and P_2 be two values of P, and let $P_1' = T(P_1)$ and $P_2' = T(P_2)$ be the two corresponding values of P'. Then from the fundamental property (p. 133) of the cross ratio we have

$$\mathcal{R}(P_\infty I, P_1 P_2) = \mathcal{R}(J' P_\infty, P_1' P_2') = \mathcal{R}(P_\infty J', P_2' P_1'),$$

which gives

$$\frac{IP_2}{IP_1} = \frac{J'P_1'}{J'P_2'}.$$

This then gives as the relation between the magnitudes of the vectors

$$IP_2 \cdot J'P_2' = IP_1 \cdot J'P_1'.$$

The vanishing point of an involution on a line which does not transform the point at infinity of the line into itself is called the *center* of the involution (p. 98). As a corollary of the above theorem we have the following:

If O is the center of an involution on a line and P, P′ is any pair of the involution, the product OP·OP′ is constant (p. 99).

65. The euclidean metric group. The euclidean metric geometry. We may now define a subgroup of the affine group which will characterize the elementary euclidean metric geometry. As may be expected from the discussion of perpendicularity in Chapter VI (p. 88) the definition of this subgroup must involve an involution on the line at infinity. Indeed, we proceed simply as follows:

Let I be an arbitrary but fixed elliptic involution on l_∞, which we call the *absolute* or *orthogonal involution*. It will simplify much of the later discussion if we assume that this involution may be considered as having two imaginary double points I_1, and I_2, called the *circular points at infinity*. The group of all projective collineations leaving the involution I invariant is called the *euclidean metric group* and the associated geometry is called the *euclidean metric geometry*. The transformations of the euclidean metric group are called *similarity transformations*; and two figures that are homologous under this group are said to be *similar*.

As to the existence of collineations leaving the absolute involution invariant, we may note that any such collineation must either leave each of the circular points I_1, I_2 invariant, or must simply interchange the points I_1, I_2; and, conversely, any collineation with either of these properties will leave the absolute involution invariant. Similarity transformations of the former type are called *direct*, those of the latter type *indirect*.

We next define two lines to be *perpendicular*, if they pass respectively through two conjugate points of the involution I (p. 88). From this definition we have at once the following:

The pairs of perpendicular lines of a pencil of lines are pairs of an elliptic involution. Through any point there is one and only one line perpendicular to a given line. A line perpendicular to one of two parallel lines is perpendicular to the other. Two lines perpendicular to the same line are parallel.

Fundamental in the treatment of the euclidean metric group are the so-called *orthogonal line reflexions*, i.e., the harmonic homologies for each of which the center L is on the line at infinity and for which the axis meets l_∞ in the point conjugate to L in the absolute involution. It is clear from the definition that the center of an orthogonal line reflexion cannot coincide with a circular point nor can its axis pass through such a point. Also, it follows at once from the definition that an orthogonal line reflexion transforms any point P into a point P' such that the line PP' is perpendicular to the axis and meets the axis in the midpoint of PP'.

66. The rectangular coordinate system. Given two points X_1, Y_1 on the line at infinity, conjugate under the absolute involution, there exist two other points U, U' on l_∞ conjugate under I and harmonic with X_1, Y_1. Let the points X_1, Y_1 be taken as the points $(1, 0, 0)$ and $(0, 1, 0)$ of a homogeneous system of coordinates and let the points U and U' be chosen as the points $(1, 1, 0)$ and $(-1, 1, 0)$, respectively. Let the point $O = (0, 0, 1)$ be any ordinary point of the plane. It is then evidently possible to choose the point $(1, 1, 1)$ in conformity with the above specifications. If now we change from the homogeneous system to a non-homogeneous system in the usual way, in which the line l_∞ is exceptional and the lines OX_1 and OY_1 are the x- and y-axes respectively, the latter are perpendicular to each other and the absolute involution is given by $x_1' = -x_2$, $x_2' = x_1$, $x_3' = x_3 = 0$. It follows that the lines $y = mx$ and $y = m'x$ are perpendicular to each other if and only if $m' = -1/m$. More generally, two lines $ax + by + c = 0$ and $a'x + b'y + c' = 0$ are perpendicular if and only if $ab' + ba' = 0$. The non-homogeneous coordinate system thus established is called a *system of rectangular coordinates*.

67. Analytic expression for the transformations of the euclidean group. The transformations of the affine group derived in §60 may be written in homogeneous form as

$$\rho x_1' = a_1 x_1 + b_1 x_2 + c_1 x_3,$$
$$\rho x_2' = a_2 x_1 + b_2 x_2 + c_2 x_3, \qquad (a_1 b_2 - a_2 b_1 \neq 0)$$
$$\rho x_3' = x_3.$$

The circular points I_1, I_2 have coordinates $(i, 1, 0)$ and $(-i, 1, 0)$, where $i^2 = -1$. Keeping in mind that the coefficients of the collineation are real (it transforms all real points into real points), the condition that $(i, 1, 0)$ is invariant gives readily $b_2 = a_1 = \alpha$, say, and $a_2 = -b_1 = \beta$, say. This leads to the following:

Any direct similarity transformation is given by

$$x' = \alpha x - \beta y + h,$$
$$y' = \beta x + \alpha y + k. \qquad (\Delta = \alpha^2 + \beta^2 > 0)$$

Similarly, the condition that $(i, 1, 0)$ be transformed into $(-i, 1, 0)$ gives $a_1 = -b_2 = \alpha$, say, and $a_2 = b_1 = \beta$, say. Hence we have the following:

Any indirect similarity transformation is given by

$$x' = \alpha x + \beta y + h,$$
$$y' = \beta x - \alpha y + k. \qquad (\Delta = -\alpha^2 - \beta^2 < 0)$$

Evidently the product of two indirect transformations is a direct transformation. This is verified by the fact that the determinant of the product of two collineations is equal to the product of their determinants and the product of two negative numbers is a positive number.

As to the orthogonal line reflexions we may readily derive the additional conditions that must be satisfied by the coefficients of our transformation. Let us suppose first that the axis of the orthogonal line reflexion passes through the origin. This implies that the point $(0, 0)$ is invariant. Since an orthogonal line reflexion is indirect our transformation is, then, of the form

$$(1) \qquad x' = \alpha x + \beta y, \qquad y' = \beta x - \alpha y.$$

If another point (m, n) on the axis is invariant this will insure that our transformation is an orthogonal line reflexion. This gives the equations $m = \alpha m + \beta n$, $n = \beta m - \alpha n$. These give for α, β the values

$$(2) \qquad \alpha = \frac{m^2 - n^2}{m^2 + n^2}, \quad \beta = \frac{2mn}{m^2 + n^2}.$$

We see at once that $\Delta = -\alpha^2 - \beta^2 = -1$. Conversely, given any transformation of type (1) with $-\alpha^2 - \beta^2 = -1$, numbers m, n can be determined so that relations (2) hold. If transformation (1) be transformed by any translation $x' = x + a$, $y' = y + b$, the result is an orthogonal line reflexion whose axis is parallel to the axis of (1). If we carry out the computation we find that

Any orthogonal line reflexion is represented by the equations

$$\begin{aligned} x' &= \alpha x + \beta y + (\alpha - 1)a + \beta b, \\ y' &= \beta x - \alpha y + \beta a - (\alpha + 1)b. \end{aligned} \qquad (\alpha^2 + \beta^2 = -1)$$

In the above equations we may without loss of generality assume $b = 0$, unless $\beta = 0$; in the latter case we may assume $a = 0$.

68. Displacements. The product of any even number of orthogonal line reflexions is called a *displacement* or a *motion*. Two figures that are homologous under a displacement are said to be *congruent*.

It is clear that the product of any even number of orthogonal line reflexions will be of the form

$$(1) \qquad \begin{aligned} x' &= \alpha x - \beta y + h, \\ y' &= \beta x + \alpha y + k. \end{aligned} \qquad (\alpha^2 + \beta^2 = 1)$$

For any such product is obviously direct and its determinant must be equal to 1. To prove that every transformation of this form is a displacement, we prove first that any translation is the product of two orthogonal line reflexions whose axes are parallel. Let the translation carry the point A into the point B and let L_∞ be the point at infinity on AB. If then L_∞' is the point conjugate to L_∞ in the absolute involution the product of two orthogonal line reflexions whose axes pass through L'_∞ will be a translation, since it leaves every point at infinity invariant. If the line reflexion whose axis is BL_∞ carries A to A', the reflexion whose axis passes through L' and the midpoint of BA' will carry A' into B. The product of these two orthogonal line reflexions is then the translation carrying A into B. Now, let D be any given transformation of form (1), and let T be the translation $x' = x + h$, $y' = y + k$. The transformation $T^{-1}D$ is then the transformation

$$(2) \qquad x' = \alpha x - \beta y, \quad y' = \beta x + \alpha y.$$

The product of the two orthogonal line reflexions

$$x' = \alpha_1 x + \beta_1 y, \quad y' = \beta_1 x - \alpha_1 y;$$
$$x' = \alpha_2 x + \beta_2 y, \quad y' = \beta_2 x - \alpha_2 y; \qquad (\alpha_1^2 + \beta_1^2 = \alpha_2^2 + \beta_2^2 = -1)$$

is the transformation

$$x' = (\alpha_1\alpha_2 + \beta_1\beta_2)x - (\beta_1\alpha_2 - \alpha_1\beta_2)y$$
$$y' = (\beta_1\alpha_2 - \alpha_1\beta_2)x + (\alpha_1\alpha_2 + \beta_1\beta_2)y.$$

This will be equivalent to (2) if

$$\alpha_1\alpha_2 + \beta_1\beta_2 = \alpha, \qquad \beta_1\alpha_2 - \alpha_1\beta_2 = \beta,$$

and these two equations can always be solved for α_2, β_2 in terms of α, β, α_1, β_1. This shows that $T^{-1}D$ is the product of two orthogonal line reflexions, and hence that D is the product of at most four orthogonal line reflexions.

A displacement which leaves any ordinary point invariant is called a *rotation*. The above discussion has shown that *any rotation leaving the origin O invariant is given by*

$$x' = \alpha x - \beta y, \qquad (\alpha^2 + \beta^2 = 1)$$
$$y' = \beta x + \alpha y.$$

It also shows that *any displacement can be represented as the resultant of a rotation about the origin and a translation.*

We may now show that any point (x_1, y_1) may be transformed by a rotation about the origin into a point on the x-axis. Indeed, if we place (x', y') in the above equations equal to $(\lambda, 0)$ and (x, y) equal to (x_1, y_1) and solve the resulting equations for α and β, we obtain

$$\alpha = \frac{\lambda x_1}{x_1^2 + y_1^2}, \qquad \beta = -\frac{\lambda y_1}{x_1^2 + y_1^2}.$$

Since $\alpha^2 + \beta^2 = 1$, this gives $\lambda = \pm\sqrt{x_1^2 + y_1^2}$. This shows further that *there is a uniquely determined rotation about the origin which transforms (x_1, y_1) into a point $(\lambda, 0)$ where λ is positive; and one which transforms (x_1, y_1) into a point $(\lambda, 0)$, where λ is negative.*

It follows also that *the only rotation about O (other than the identity) which leaves a line through O invariant is given by $x' = -x$, $y' = -y$.*

The product of an odd number of orthogonal line reflexions is called a *symmetry*. It is clear that the set of all displacements forms a group which is invariant under the euclidean metric group; and that the set of all displacements and symmetries forms a group which is invariant under the euclidean metric group. This justifies the following definitions: Two figures that are homologous under a displacement are said to be *congruent*; two figures homologous under a symmetry are said to be *symmetric*.

As an illustration we may derive one of the three theorems on the congruence of triangles with which most elementary texts begin the study of geometry.

Two triangles ABC and A'B'C' are congruent in such a way that A corresponds to A', and B to B', if the point pair AB is congruent to A'B' and the ordered line pairs ca and cb are congruent to the ordered line pairs c'a' and c'b' respectively.

In the statement of the theorem the line a is the line BC, etc. in the usual notation, and we have had to use "ordered line pair" in place of angle, since the latter concept has not yet been defined. By hypothesis, there exists a displacement T which transforms A into A' and B into B'. Suppose $T(a) = a''$, $T(b) = b''$, and $T(C) = C''$. If $a'' \neq a'$, we should have the pair $c'a'$ congruent to $c'a''$ and there would have to be a displacement leaving B' and c' invariant and transforming a' into a''. If we think of B' as the point O of the theorem above (p. 168) this displacement would have to be the identity or the rotation of the above theorem, and both these suppositions contradict the hypothesis that $a'' \neq a'$. Similarly we can prove $b'' = b'$, and hence $C'' = C'$.

69. The circle. As a further illustration we may give a definition of a circle in accordance with the usual definition of elementary geometry. If O and A are any two distinct points the *circle* with O as *center* and OA as *radius* is the locus of all points P such that OP is congruent to OA.

If O is taken as the origin of a set of rectangular coordinates, in which OA is the positive side of the x-axis, and if a is the coordinate of A and (x, y) the coordinates of the variable point P, the equation of the circle is $x^2 + y^2 = a^2$ (p. 168). If the center is the point (h, k), the translation $x' = x + h$, $y' = y + k$ will transform this circle into

$$(x - h)^2 + (y - k)^2 = a^2.$$

The equation of any circle in the plane is then of the form

$$x^2 + y^2 + mx + ny + p = 0.$$

If this be written in homogeneous form, it is seen at once that the two circular points $(i, 1, 0)$ and $(-i, 1, 0)$ satisfy any equation of this form. Conversely, any (real) conic is represented by an equation of the second degree with real coefficients. If the general equation of the second degree with real coefficients be subjected to the condition that it shall be satisfied by the circular points it assumes the form above. Hence, *the necessary and sufficient condition that a conic be a circle is that it shall contain the circular points at infinity*. We have here the reason for calling the double points of the absolute involution circular.

70. Distance. We defined the magnitude of a vector OB as its ratio to a unit vector OA collinear with it (p. 159). This is a concept belonging to the affine

geometry. But in this geometry no relation exists between the magnitudes of non-collinear vectors. The
euclidean metric group, however, makes it possible to
establish such a relation. We need only specify that
any two unit vectors OA and $O'A'$ shall be congruent.
In other words, given a unit vector OA and the circle
with O as center and OA as radius, any other unit vector
must be equal to a vector OP where P is on this circle.
Since P', where $OP' = -OP$, is also on this circle
(p. 168), this gives two choices for the unit vector of
any system of collinear vectors, each of two possible
unit vectors being the negative of the other. It is
possible therefore to compare only the absolute values
of the magnitudes of noncollinear vectors; there is no
way of distinguishing their algebraic signs. This absolute value we call distance. It may be defined as follows: Let OA be an arbitrary pair of distinct points
which is to be called the *unit of distance*. The *distance*
from any point P to any point Q is then the number
corresponding to that point D of the line OA such that
PQ is congruent to OD, and such that in the scale determined on OA by $O=0$, $A=1$, and $P_\infty = \infty$ (where
P_∞ is the point at infinity on OA) the point D has a positive coordinate. The distance from P to Q may be denoted by $\mathrm{Dist}(PQ)$.

It follows at once that $\mathrm{Dist}(PQ)$ is uniquely defined and positive when $P \neq Q$ and is 0 when $P=Q$;
moreover, $\mathrm{Dist}(PQ) = \mathrm{Dist}(QP)$. Also, if A, B, C are
any three points on a line so that B is between A and
C, we have

$$\mathrm{Dist}(AB) + \mathrm{Dist}(BC) = \mathrm{Dist}(AC).$$

71. Length of arc of a circle. We may also indicate briefly how the length or the circumference of a circle or the length of any arc of circle is defined. Let P_1, P_2, P_3, $\cdots$, P_n be n points in the order $P_1P_2P_3 \cdots P_n$ on a circle. If we place

$$p = \text{Dist}(P_1P_2) + \text{Dist}(P_2P_3) + \cdots + \text{Dist}(P_nP_1),$$

it may be proved that for a given circle the numbers p obtained for all possible choices of the points P_i do not exceed a certain number. The number c which is the smallest number larger than all the numbers p is called the *length* or the *circumference* of the circle. It is then possible to show that if c and c' are the lengths of two circles with centers O and O' and with radii OP and $O'P'$ respectively, we have

$$\frac{c}{c'} = \frac{\text{Dist}(OP)}{\text{Dist}(O'P')}.$$

If we choose $O'P'$ as the unit of distance and denote $\text{Dist}(OP)$ by r, we have

$$c = 2\pi r,$$

where we have denoted the constant c' by 2π.

In a similar fashion we may define the *length of arc* of a circle, where by the arc PQ we mean one of the two parts of the circle into which it is divided by the two distinct points P and Q. To this end we confine the points P_i to be points of the arc in question, and proceed as before. It may then be shown that if B is any point of the arc AC and if by arc AB and arc BC we mean the arcs contained in arc AC, then

length of arc AB + length of arc BC = length of arc AC.

72. Angle. Any point O of an ordinary line in a euclidean plane divides the line into two parts each of which is called a *ray* (or *half-line*) *issuing from O*. The two rays issuing from a point O on the same line are said to be *opposite*. The figure formed by two rays issuing from a point O is called an *angle*; the point O is called the *vertex* and the rays are called the *sides* of the angle.

We are now in a position to introduce the measure of an angle. Let a given angle have the vertex O and sides OA and OM and let A' be any other point on the ray OA. Let the circles with center at O and radii OA and OA' meet the other side of the angle in the points B and B', and let arc AB be one of the arcs into which A, B divide the first circle. If P is any point of this arc the ray OP will meet the second circle in a point P'. Let the arc $A'B'$ be the one containing P'. We may then prove that if s, s' are the lengths of the arcs AB and $A'B'$ as above defined and r, r' are the distances OA and OA' respectively, we have $s'/r'=s/r$. This ratio may then be taken as the measure of the angle. The procedure is familiar and we need give no further details.

It is now possible to define the trigonometric functions in the usual way as the ratios of certain distances with the usual conventions as to signs. We assume in the future that this can be done.

It would have been possible to approach the measure of an angle from a different point of view. Suppose the sides of an angle whose vertex is O meet the line at infinity in the two points P, Q; and let the sides of another angle with vertex O' meet the line at infinity in the points P', Q'. The ordered pair of lines OP, OQ will be congruent to the ordered pair $O'P'$, $O'Q'$, if and only if

$$\mathcal{R}(PQ,\ I_1 I_2) = \mathcal{R}(P'Q',\ I_1 I_2),$$

where I_1, I_2 are the two circular points. This suggests that $\mathcal{R}(l_1 l_2,\ i_1 i_2) = \mathcal{R}(PQ,\ I_1 I_2)$, where l_1, l_2, i_1, i_2 denote the lines OP, OQ, OI_1, OI_2 respectively, could be used as a measure of the angle whose sides are on l_1, l_2; more precisely, that it could be used as a measure for the ordered line pair $l_1 l_2$. It is a number which is uniquely defined by any ordered line pair and which remains unchanged if the pair is replaced by any congruent pair. We should, however, wish to have our measure m satisfy the relation

$$m(l_1 l_2) + m(l_2 l_3) = m(l_1 l_3),$$

if l_1, l_2, l_3 are concurrent lines, and this relation is not satisfied by the corresponding cross ratios. In fact we have

$$\mathcal{R}(l_1 l_2,\ i_1 i_2) \cdot R(l_2 l_3,\ i_1 i_2) = R(l_1 l_3,\ i_1 i_2),$$

as is easily verified. This shows that if we place

$$(1) \qquad m(l_1, l_2) = c \log \mathcal{R}(l_1 l_2, i_1 i_2),$$

where c is an arbitrary constant, the desired relation will hold. That this measure is indeed equivalent to the measure for angles already introduced may be easily seen if we assume Euler's relation

$$\cos \theta + i \sin \theta = e^{i\theta}.$$

If as before l_1, l_2 meet the line at infinity in P, Q and if, with respect to a rectangular system of coordinates the coordinates of P, Q, I_1, I_2 are taken as $(p, 1, 0)$, $(q, 1, 0)$, $(i, 1, 0)$, $(-i, 1, 0)$, we have

$$\mathcal{R}(l_1 l_2, \ i_1 i_2) = \mathcal{R}(PQ, \ I_1 I_2) = \frac{p-i}{p+i} : \frac{q-i}{q+i}.$$

If the polar form of the complex number $p+i$ is $r_1(\cos \theta_1 + i \sin \theta_1)$ and of $q+i$ is $r_2(\cos \theta_2 + i \sin \theta_2)$, this cross ratio becomes $e^{2i(\theta_2 - \theta_1)}$. If now we place $\theta_2 - \theta_1 = \theta$, we have

$$\log \mathcal{R}(l_1 l_2, \ i_1 i_2) = 2i\theta.$$

If then we choose the constant c in (1) to be $-i/2$ we have finally

$$(2) \qquad m(l_1 l_2) = -\frac{i}{2} \log \mathcal{R}(l_1 l_2), \ i_1 i_2) = \theta.$$

This formula, which defines the measure of an angle in terms of imaginary lines will be found of interest because of its analogy with similar formulas in the so-called non-euclidean geometries, to which we now turn our attention.

73. The non-euclidean geometries. A real conic divides the real points of a projective plane into three classes, the *interior points*, the *exterior points*, and the *points on the conic*. The interior points are characterized by the fact that any real line through an interior point meets the conic in two real distinct points, while through an exterior point there exist real lines which do not meet the conic in real points. Through any exterior point two real distinct tangents to the conic may be drawn, while through an interior point no real tangents to the conic exist. Evidently, any real collineation which leaves a conic invariant will transform interior points into interior points.

Let there be given a real conic in the projective plane. This conic we call the *absolute conic* or simply *the absolute*. The group of all collineations in the plane leaving this conic invariant we call the *hyperbolic metric group* and the corresponding geometry we call the *hyperbolic metric geometry* in the plane. The interior points of the conic are called *ordinary points* and the points on the absolute or exterior to it are called *ideal* points. A line containing only ideal points is an *ideal line*; if a line contains more than one ordinary point, all the ordinary points of the line constitute an *ordinary line*. The ordinary points and ordinary lines constitute the so-called *hyperbolic plane*. Two lines containing ordinary points are said to be *parallel* if they have a point of the absolute in common; *perpendicular* if they are conjugate with respect to the absolute. Two figures of the hyperbolic plane are said to be *congruent*, if they are homologous under a transformation of the hyperbolic metric group.

The geometry corresponding to this group and the above definitions has many propositions in common with the euclidean metric geometry. For example, two distinct ordinary points are on one and only one ordinary line; two distinct ordinary lines cannot meet in more than one ordinary point; through a given ordinary point there is one and only one ordinary line perpendicular to a given ordinary line. The fundamental properties of congruence, of order, and of continuity are the same in the hyperbolic as in the euclidean geometry. But the propositions regarding parallels are radically different in the two geometries. In fact it is evident from the above definitions that *through an ordinary point not on a given ordinary line there are two parallels to the given line and an infinite number of ordinary lines not meeting the given line.*

The so-called parallel postulate of Euclid has been the occasion of much study and speculation from the time of Euclid onward. This postulate is equivalent to the proposition of euclidean geometry that through a given point not on a given line there is one and only one parallel to the given line. Euclid himself does not seem to have been altogether satisfied with it. He avoids using it as long as possible in his *Elements*. His immediate successors attacked the problem of proving the parallel postulate on the basis of his other postulates, and through all the centuries that followed, in which any geometric activity was noticeable, we find this problem engaging the attention of geometers. It came to be suspected that the solution of the problem was impossible. Finally, JOHANN BOLYAI (1832) and N. I. LOBATCHEVSKI (1829), independently of each other, published a self-consistent body of geometric theorems based on a postulate which implied that more than one parallel could be drawn through a given point to a given line. This constituted the first of the so-called non-euclidean geometries. Some years later (1851) BERNHARD RIEMANN showed the possibility of a second type of non-euclidean geometry—the so-called *elliptic geometry*—in which through a given point there exists no line parallel to a given line. That both the hyperbolic geometry of Bolyai-Lobatchevski and the elliptic geometry of Riemann may be defined as geometries associated with subgroups of the projective group was first shown by ARTHUR CAYLEY (1859), although he did not formulate his ideas on the basis of group-theoretic considerations. It may be recalled that it was Cayley who exclaimed: "Projective geometry is all geometry."

A formula for the distance between two points of the hyperbolic plane and one for the angle between two lines of this plane may readily be derived. The analogy with a previous formula (p. 175) is at once apparent and reflects the analogy between the euclidean and the hyperbolic geometries. Let A and B be two ordinary points and let the line AB meet the absolute in the points A_∞ and B_∞, the notation being so chosen that the points are in the order $A_\infty ABB_\infty$. If $A', B', A_\infty' B_\infty'$ are another set of points similarly determined, it is easily shown that the ordered point pair AB will be congruent to the ordered pair $A'B'$ if and only if we have

$$\mathcal{R}(AB,\ A_\infty B_\infty) = \mathcal{R}(A'B',\ A_\infty' B_\infty').$$

We accordingly define the distance between A and B by means of the equation

$$\mathrm{Dist}(AB) = k \log \mathcal{R}(AB,\ A_\infty B_\infty).$$

The cross ratio involved in this definition has, with the notation assigned, a positive value and hence its logarithm has a real value. This real value of the logarithm is defined as the distance in question. It follows readily that we have

$$\mathrm{Dist}(AB) = \mathrm{Dist}(BA)\ ;$$

and that if A, B, C are collinear ordinary points in the order A, B, C we have

$$\mathrm{Dist}(AB) + \mathrm{Dist}(BC) = \mathrm{Dist}(AC).$$

The constant k may be determined by choosing a fixed point pair OP as the unit of distance. It may be noted that under this definition of distance the ordinary line is of infinite length.

By analogy (and also by duality, since the absolute conic is a self-dual figure) we define the measure of an angle. Let a, b be any two ordinary lines intersecting in an ordinary point O and let i_1, i_2 be the two (imaginary) tangents to the absolute through O. We then define the measure of the ordered line pair ab to be

$$\theta = m(ab) = -\frac{i}{2} \log \mathcal{R}(ab, \ i_1 i_2).$$

The so-called *elliptic metric geometry* is the geometry associated with the group of real collineations which leaves an imaginary conic invariant. That such a group, the *elliptic metric group*, exists we will take for granted, although there is little difficulty in establishing its existence (analytically, for example). All the real points of the projective plane are ordinary points. Every two ordinary lines intersect in an ordinary point, i.e., there are no ordinary parallel lines. Two lines are *perpendicular* if they are conjugate with respect to the absolute conic, etc. The formulas for distance and angle are entirely analogous to those just developed for the hyperbolic geometry, though certain modifications are necessary because the absolute conic is now imaginary.

Enough has been said, it is hoped, to give the reader some idea of how these non-euclidean geometries arise and their relation to the ordinary euclidean geometry.

The terms *hyperbolic* and *elliptic* applied to these noneuclidean geometries arise (by analogy with the classification of projectivities on a line) because a line containing ordinary points meets the absolute in two distinct real points in case of the hyperbolic geometry, while in the elliptic geometry such a line meets the absolute in a pair of conjugate imaginary points. The euclidean geometry is often called the *parabolic metric geometry*, by analogy with the preceding terminology, a real line meeting the line at infinity (the absolute for this case) in a single (real) point. In fact it can be shown that the euclidean geometry may be considered as a limiting case both of the hyperbolic and the elliptic geometries.

The reader interested in a further study of non-euclidean geometry may be referred to the following: For further details of the projective treatment here only sketched he may consult, VEBLEN and YOUNG, *Projective Geometry*, vol. II, Chapter VIII; for an elementary historical sketch and a concrete representation of the hyperbolic geometry he may be referred to J. W. YOUNG, *Lectures on the Fundamental Concepts of Algebra and Geometry*, New York, 1911, Lectures II and III; for a more detailed history and an exposition of some of the content, to R. BONOLA, *Non-euclidean Geometry*, English translation by Carslaw, Chicago, 1912. Other texts in English are by J. L. COOLIDGE, Oxford, 1909; and H. P. MANNING, Boston, 1901.

INDEX

(Numbers refer to pages; f after a number means "and following".)

INDEX

Separation, of pairs of points, 45; of harmonic pairs, 46

Side(s), of a triangle, 27; of a complete quadrangle or quadrilateral, 28; opposite, 28; of a simple hexagon, 65; opposite, 65; of an angle, 173

Similar figures, 163

Similarity transformations, 163

Simple, quadrangle, 30, 71; pentagon, 70; hexagon, 65

Simply transitive, 109

Smith, D. E., 10

Space, projective, 8, 19f

Staudt, Ch. von, 120

Subgroup, 108

Subtraction, 122

Sum of vectors, 158

Symmetric, 169

Symmetry, 18, 168

Tangent(s), to a point conic, 63, 69; form a conic line, 73

Tetrahedron, 29

Throws, algebra of, 120

Transform of a transformation, 111

Transformation, perspective, 5, 14, 40; projective, 5, 42; transform of, 111; between two-dimensional (three-dimensional) forms, 112; group of, 107; similarity, 163; symbolic representation of, 105f

Transitive, simply, 109

Translation, 155; group of 154f; parallel to a line, 155; analytic representation of, 157

Triangle(s), 6, 7; perspective, 8, 34; definition of, 27

Unit, vector, 159, 171; distance, 171

Vanishing points, 161

Veblen, Oswald, 25, 67, 152, 180

Vector(s), 158; null, 158; sum of, 158; ratio of, 159; magnitude of, 159; unit, 159, 171

Vertex (vertices), of a triangle, 27; of a complete quadrangle or quadrilateral, 28; opposite, 28; of a tetrahedron, 29; of a simple hexagon, 65; opposite, 65; of a conic, 101; of an angle, 173

X-axis, 135

X-coordinate, 135

Y-axis, 135

Y-coordinate, 136

Young, J. W., 25, 67, 152, 180

[PRINTED IN U.S.A.]